This guide covers all areas of GCSE Electronic Products, including design, skills, components, materials, techniques, production processes, analysis and evaluation. In doing so it encompasses much of the GCSE Resistant Materials course. It also offers guidance on how to tackle new projects and illustrates the various stages of the design process, following the development of an example product from brief to manufacture.

Covering the core elements of all the major specifications, The Essentials of Design and Technology: Electronic Products is an invaluable course companion and exam revision aid. The material has been expertly written and meticulously checked, so it can be relied on to cover everything you need to know to pass the course and achieve your full potential. The information is presented in small, relevant chunks that are easy to understand and absorb, and clear diagrams are used throughout to illustrate key concepts and ideas.

DAVID McHUGH

David McHugh is both a Chief Examiner and Principal Moderator for GCSE Design and Technology Electronic Products. David has over 30 years of teaching experience and has taught the subject to A-level standard. He has worked in a variety of schools and colleges and is an educational consultant for Design and Technology to several Local Education Authorities.

Known nationally for leading teacher INSET meetings and courses, David is a well-respected trainer in the field of Electronics. He has rightly gained a reputation for his practical, down-to-earth approach to the teaching of this important area of the school curriculum.

With special thanks to Barbara McHugh and Jon-David McHugh for all their help and assistance in producing this guide.

Many thanks to Rapid Electronics for supplying the images of the components.

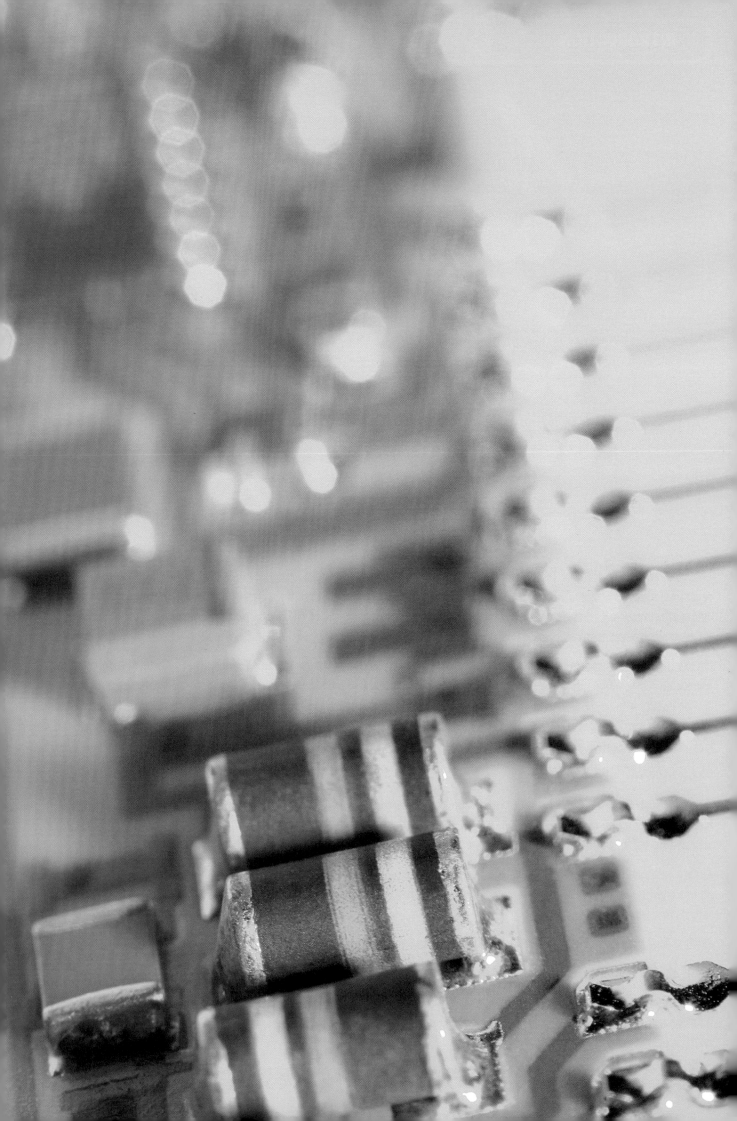

● CONTENTS

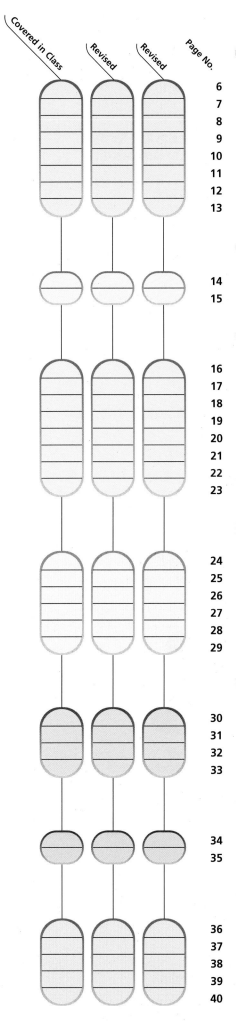

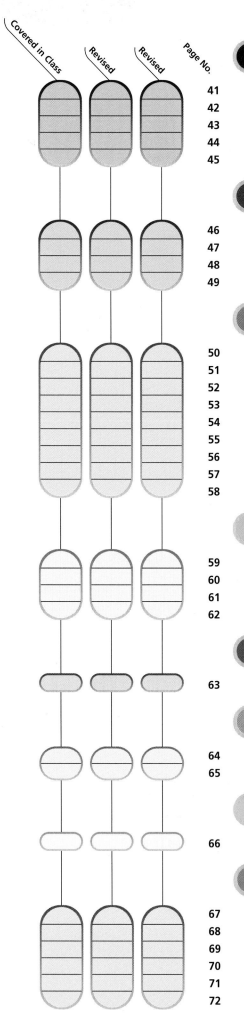

CONTENTS

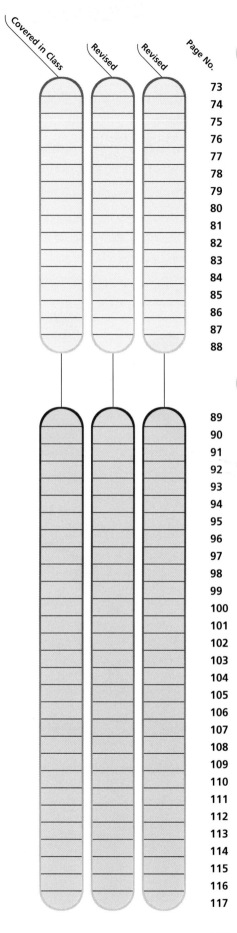

Components Continued

Interfacing

Electronic Products

GCSE Electronic Products is a product design-based course which will allow you to specialise in an area of Design and Technology where you will learn about designing, making and evaluating quality products.

Electronic Products is special in that it requires you to work with electronic components and a range of resistant materials throughout the course. You will use electronic components and construction methods when making your electronic circuits and use appropriate resistant materials to case the electronics.

Although you will be studying a course which consists of electronics and resistant materials, you must always remember that the course is Electronic Products and not Resistant Materials Technology. You must, therefore, always spend a greater amount of time studying the electronics content of the course. Here are some examples of electronic products you could make.

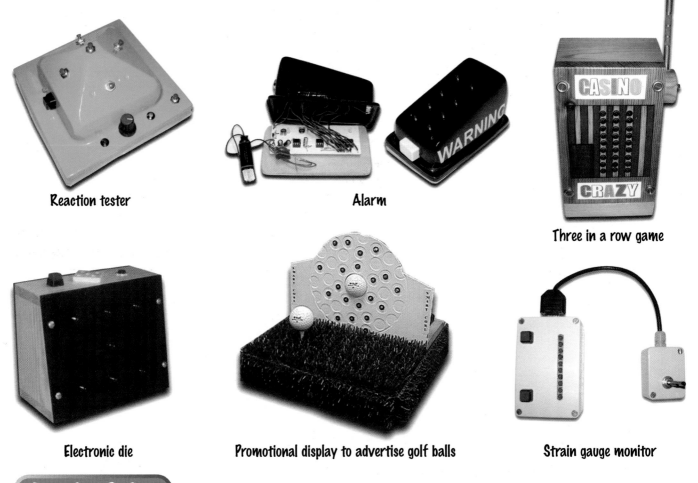

Reaction tester

Alarm

Three in a row game

Electronic die

Promotional display to advertise golf balls

Strain gauge monitor

Awarding Bodies

Your school will enter you for a GCSE course with one of the following AWARDING BODIES. Each one of these has a website where you can access information about what you will be taught and how you will be assessed.

- Assessment and Qualifications Alliance, usually known as AQA - www.aqa.org.uk
- Oxford Cambridge and RSA Examinations, usually known as OCR - www.ocr.org.uk
- Edexcel - www.edexcel.org.uk

In addition to the English Awarding Bodies, there are separate ones for Northern Ireland and Wales. AQA and OCR have both produced a SPECIFICATION FOR DESIGN AND TECHNOLOGY: ELECTRONIC PRODUCTS which follow similar guidelines. Edexcel has produced a Systems and Control Specification which includes the study of Electronic Products. This Revision Guide will provide useful advice and information for whichever Awarding Body your school is using. Ask your teacher which Awarding Body Specification you are following for Electronic Products.

Foundation Or Higher Tier?

The written examination will take place at the end of the course, in May or June of Year 11, and will make up **40%** of the total GCSE marks. You will be entered for either the FOUNDATION TIER or the HIGHER TIER written paper. The Foundation Tier covers grades G to C and the Higher Tier paper covers grades D to A*. However, grade E can be awarded to pupils who are entered for the Higher Tier but perform below expectations. Pupils who do not achieve grade E on the Higher Tier will be recorded as Ungraded. If you are entered for the Foundation Tier of the written paper, the highest grade available to you is grade C, no matter how high the grade you achieve on your coursework project. Remember, it is the written paper which is tiered, not the coursework project.

The Higher Tier paper is intended for pupils who are expected to gain grade C or above. Your teacher is likely to enter you for the Foundation Tier paper unless you appear to be on target for at least a grade B in your coursework project. Examination entries are usually carried out in January of Year 11, which is well before the date for completing your coursework project. Pupils who are behind schedule with their coursework at this stage may well be entered for the Foundation Tier, so do not leave your coursework until the last few weeks.

What To Expect

Most Awarding Bodies set a single written examination paper, although some set two. Typically the examination lasts for about two hours in total, so you will need to prepare thoroughly for this part of the assessment. Some Awarding Bodies provide you with a theme for part of the written paper. Ask your teacher if your written paper is going to be based on a theme.

It is the Chief Examiner's job to set a written paper which will test your knowledge, skills and understanding of designing and making quality electronic products. As a general guide, questions are planned to earn a mark a minute. So if you have a ten mark question, you are expected to spend about ten minutes on that question. The written paper consists of a range of compulsory questions. There will be no choice of questions. The written paper is important because it accounts for **40%** of the GCSE marks. The written paper can therefore raise, confirm or lower the grade you achieve on your coursework project. The written paper will reflect the emphasis towards electronics and will test skills which are also tested in the coursework project. Examples include:

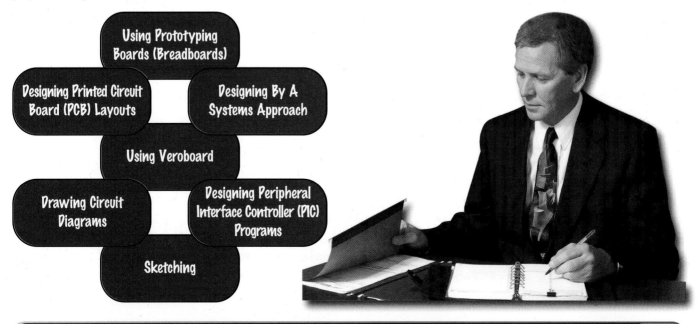

Using Prototyping Boards (Breadboards)

Designing Printed Circuit Board (PCB) Layouts

Designing By A Systems Approach

Using Veroboard

Drawing Circuit Diagrams

Designing Peripheral Interface Controller (PIC) Programs

Sketching

The questions on the written paper will reflect the Electronic Products subject content and will include the following:

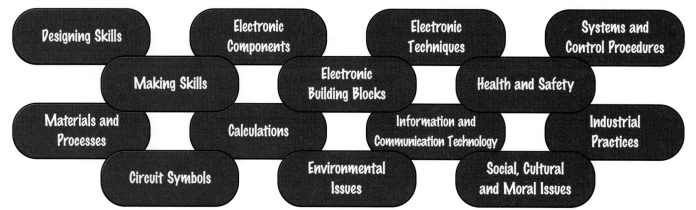

Designing Skills | Electronic Components | Electronic Techniques | Systems and Control Procedures

Making Skills | Electronic Building Blocks | Health and Safety

Materials and Processes | Calculations | Information and Communication Technology | Industrial Practices

Circuit Symbols | Environmental Issues | Social, Cultural and Moral Issues

Not all of the subject content can appear in any one written paper. It is therefore the job of the Chief Examiner to make sure that all of the subject content is covered over a period of three years. Look at previous written examination papers and become familiar with the style and the wording of the questions and the space available to answer the questions. You will notice that some parts of the subject content appear more frequently than others and, equally, some parts are easier than others.

'Easy Mark' Questions

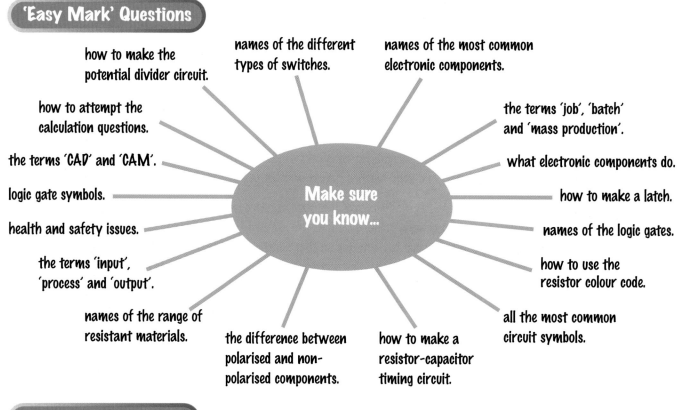

Make sure you know…

- how to make the potential divider circuit.
- names of the different types of switches.
- names of the most common electronic components.
- how to attempt the calculation questions.
- the terms 'CAD' and 'CAM'.
- logic gate symbols.
- health and safety issues.
- the terms 'input', 'process' and 'output'.
- names of the range of resistant materials.
- the difference between polarised and non-polarised components.
- how to make a resistor-capacitor timing circuit.
- the terms 'job', 'batch' and 'mass production'.
- what electronic components do.
- how to make a latch.
- names of the logic gates.
- how to use the resistor colour code.
- all the most common circuit symbols.

Calculation Questions

There are five marks available for calculation questions. Below you will find a breakdown of how the marks are allocated.

Resistors in series

$R_{total} = R_1 + R_2 + R_3$

$R_{total} = 1K + 2K2 + 1K$

$R_{total} = 4K2$

- Copying the correct formula from the front of the examination paper. 1 mark
- Entering the values. 1 mark
- Transposing the formula if needed. 1 mark
- Giving the correct answer with units. 2 marks

Potential divider

$V_s = \dfrac{R_2}{R_1 + R_2} \times V$

$V_s = \dfrac{10}{10 + 10} \times 9$

$V_s = 4.5 \text{ volts}$

'How To...' Questions

Make sure you are prepared for 'how to...' questions. Here are some examples of the type of questions you may be asked in the written examination.

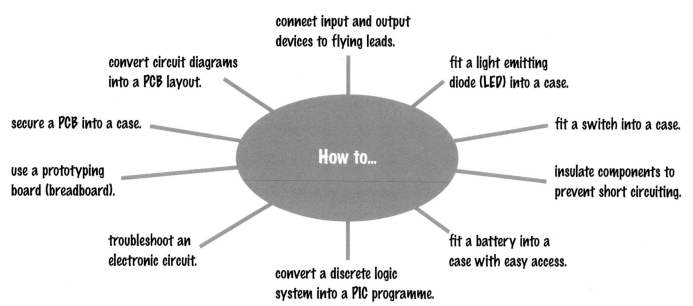

connect input and output devices to flying leads.

convert circuit diagrams into a PCB layout.

fit a light emitting diode (LED) into a case.

secure a PCB into a case.

fit a switch into a case.

use a prototyping board (breadboard).

insulate components to prevent short circuiting.

How to...

troubleshoot an electronic circuit.

fit a battery into a case with easy access.

convert a discrete logic system into a PIC programme.

'Use Sketches And Notes' Questions

Always sketch in 3D – suitable projections are ISOMETRIC, OBLIQUE and PERSPECTIVE. This is an example of an isometric projection.

- Although not essential, colour can enhance the quality of the sketch.
- Add as much detail as possible.
- Show and label construction methods.
- Label the materials used.
- Label the fixing devices.
- Add dimensions.
- Use all the space available.

'Logic Diagrams And Truth Tables' Questions

Only one-input and two-input logic gates should be used to solve logic problems in the written paper. This is because only one-input and two-input logic gates are included in the subject content of the specification.

AND gate symbol

AND gate truth table

A	B	Q
0	0	0
0	1	0
1	0	0
1	1	1

- The correct use of logic gate symbols gains marks.
- Knowledge of logic gate truth tables gains marks.
- Quality drawing of logic diagrams gains marks.

'Drawing Circuit Diagrams' Questions

- Draw the circuit symbols in proportion, eg. a fixed resistor symbol should be approximately three times longer than the width.
- Draw the circuit symbols accurately.
- Show all joined solder dots (connections).
- Label the components with values if given.
- Indicate the polarity of any polar components.

Make sure you use a sharp pencil and work accurately - circuit diagrams which are drawn with a blunt pencil and which are too small are difficult to mark.

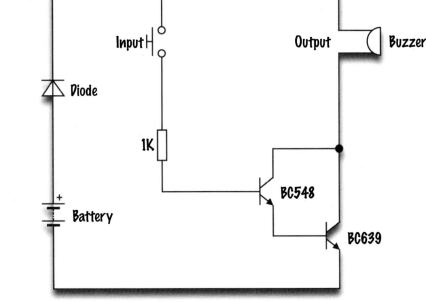

DARLINGTON DRIVER CIRCUIT (See page 84).

'Drawing PCB Track Layout Diagrams' Questions

- Make the outside and inside diameters of the pads the same size as those shown on the examination paper.
- Draw the pads clearly and with a centre hole.
- Label the plus volts and zero volts power rails.
- Label all component positions.
- Draw the tracks the same thickness as those shown on the examination paper.
- Label the position of pin 1 on the ICs.
- Label and position any wire jumper links.
- A zero ohm resistor makes an ideal jumper link.
- Marks are not generally lost by using jumper links.

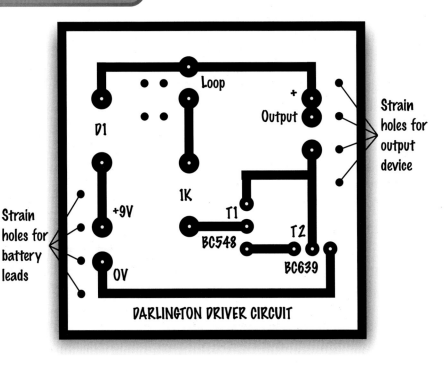

DARLINGTON DRIVER CIRCUIT

'Describe And Explain' Questions

- Use the space available. If the answer extends beyond the space given, it is likely to be too detailed or confused.
- Use technical language appropriate to the Electronic Products Specification.
- Use the format suggested in the question - answer in the same order.
- If no format is given in the question, always answer in terms of INPUT, PROCESS and OUTPUT.

Preparation Of Coursework

You will be required to produce a COURSEWORK PROJECT. This will involve designing and making an electronic product which consists of electronic circuitry packaged in a resistant materials case. The project should represent 40 hours of your lesson time and include a concise DESIGN FOLDER and a 3D PRODUCT.

The design folder should explain the problem or task you choose to look into, the analysis and research you gather, the specification for the product, your design ideas and how you develop them towards a final design proposal, and the testing and evaluation you carry out.

Your coursework project accounts for 60% of your final GCSE mark - 40% of the total GCSE marks are allocated to the making of the product and 20% are allocated to the quality of your design folder.

40 hours to design and make an electronic product is not a lot of time. You will have to be careful how you manage and use your time. Before you start your project, it is a good idea to make a time plan of the tasks you have to carry out.

Remember you will have to design and make an electronic circuit and a case within 40 hours. You will also need to balance the time you spend on developing and making the electronics part of your project against the time required for the casing. Keep in mind that your project is an electronic product and therefore greater emphasis must be given to the electronics. As a guide, a ratio of 60:40 in favour of the electronics should deliver the balance to satisfy the coursework requirements of the Electronic Products specification.

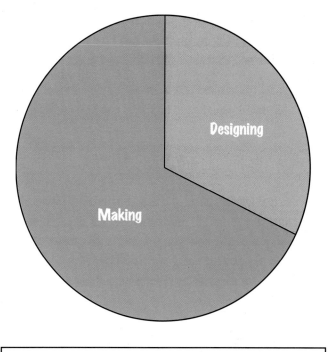

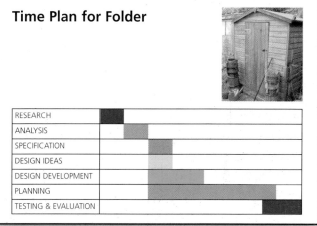

Time Plan for Folder

RESEARCH			
ANALYSIS			
SPECIFICATION			
DESIGN IDEAS			
DESIGN DEVELOPMENT			
PLANNING			
TESTING & EVALUATION			

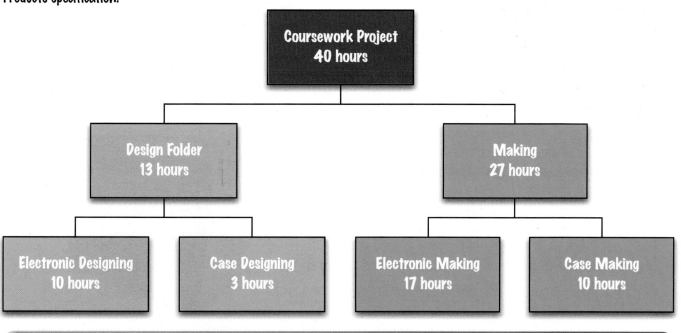

Coursework Project
40 hours

Design Folder
13 hours

Making
27 hours

Electronic Designing
10 hours

Case Designing
3 hours

Electronic Making
17 hours

Case Making
10 hours

To make sure your design folder is concise you will have to be selective in deciding what to include. Do not pad out the design folder with irrelevant material. It is the quality of the design folder that gains the marks, not the quantity.

As your coursework project makes up a massive 60% of your total GCSE marks, try very hard to complete it. Many pupils spend too long on the design folder and then have too little time to finish making the electronic product. Ask your teacher for a copy of the ASSESSMENT CRITERIA and make sure that you attempt each stage.

Your coursework project will be marked by your teacher and then re-marked by a moderator from the Awarding Body. The moderator might adjust your teacher's marks up or down or accept them.

The Moderator's Advice

The Principal Moderator is in charge of the assessment of coursework and sets a standard for each GCSE grade. The Principal Moderator checks that all moderators assess to the same standard. Unlike your teacher, the moderator will not have the opportunity of seeing how you progress with your project. They will not be able to talk to you or ask you questions but must make their assessment based on the evidence you provide. Your design folder and the notes and drawings you provide are a vital part of the assessment process. Do not assume that the moderator will understand what you are thinking - make your thoughts and ideas clear.

So that the moderator will be able to follow your design development, organise your design folder so the work is set out logically and clearly. Make sure your written work is easy to read and the meaning clear. Check your spelling, punctuation and grammar. Try to use technical language appropriate to the Electronic Products specification. Remember -marks are awarded for the quality of the presentation of your design folder.

What To Include In Your Design Folder

- A brief explanation of the project, which should include a DESIGN BRIEF.
- Details of the RESEARCH that you need to undertake.
- Your ANALYSIS of the problem and the research material you collect.
- A SPECIFICATION for the product.
- A range of INITIAL IDEAS which meet this specification.
- The DEVELOPMENT of one idea.
- A FINAL DESIGN PROPOSAL and workplan in enough detail for the moderator to follow.
- TESTING and EVALUATIONS throughout the design folder.
- The QUALITY ASSURANCE checks you need to make.
- How the product would be manufactured commercially.

The design folder should show your industrial understanding and your ability to communicate your thinking. It is expected that you use a variety of INFORMATION AND COMMUNICATION TECHNOLOGY (ICT) wherever it is appropriate to do so. You should also show an understanding of SYSTEMS AND CONTROL.

Altogether you should spend about 13 hours of your time working on the design folder ...

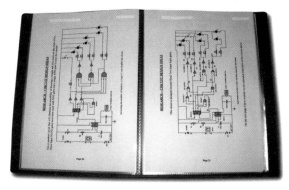

... and the remaining 27 hours making a quality electronic product.

This flow chart is to help you understand the design process as it exists in industry to help you apply these principles to your project work.

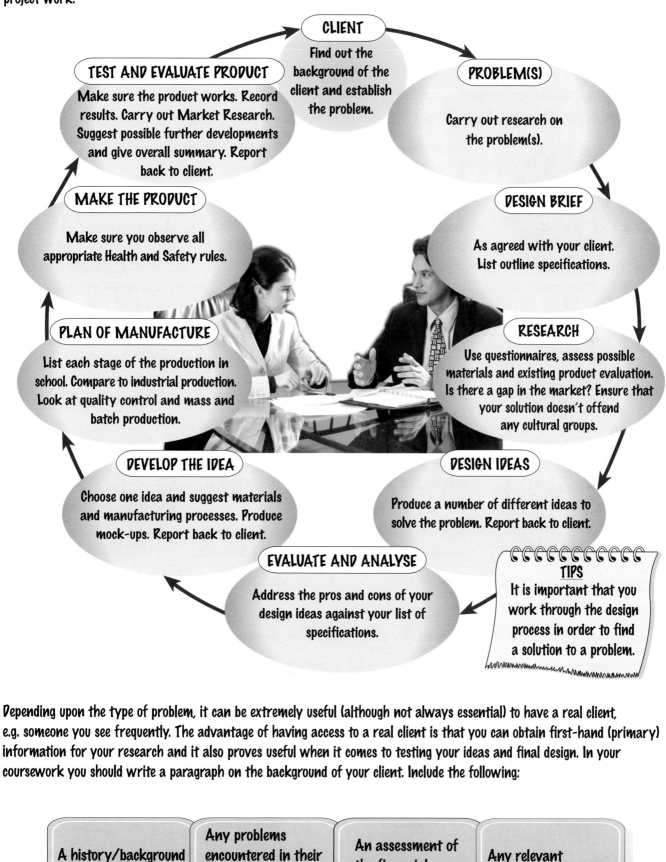

CLIENT
Find out the background of the client and establish the problem.

PROBLEM(S)
Carry out research on the problem(s).

TEST AND EVALUATE PRODUCT
Make sure the product works. Record results. Carry out Market Research. Suggest possible further developments and give overall summary. Report back to client.

DESIGN BRIEF
As agreed with your client. List outline specifications.

MAKE THE PRODUCT
Make sure you observe all appropriate Health and Safety rules.

RESEARCH
Use questionnaires, assess possible materials and existing product evaluation. Is there a gap in the market? Ensure that your solution doesn't offend any cultural groups.

PLAN OF MANUFACTURE
List each stage of the production in school. Compare to industrial production. Look at quality control and mass and batch production.

DEVELOP THE IDEA
Choose one idea and suggest materials and manufacturing processes. Produce mock-ups. Report back to client.

DESIGN IDEAS
Produce a number of different ideas to solve the problem. Report back to client.

EVALUATE AND ANALYSE
Address the pros and cons of your design ideas against your list of specifications.

TIPS
It is important that you work through the design process in order to find a solution to a problem.

Depending upon the type of problem, it can be extremely useful (although not always essential) to have a real client, e.g. someone you see frequently. The advantage of having access to a real client is that you can obtain first-hand (primary) information for your research and it also proves useful when it comes to testing your ideas and final design. In your coursework you should write a paragraph on the background of your client. Include the following:

A history/background including any social and cultural issues.	Any problems encountered in their daily routine which relate to the design problem.	An assessment of the financial limitations on the project.	Any relevant photographic material (primary research).

How Should I Start My Project?

Choosing a project or identifying a problem or a need can be difficult, especially with projects that include electronics. Therefore, a number of Awarding Bodies help you by providing a list of suitable coursework projects. Discuss this with your teacher or go on to the Awarding Bodies' websites and see what is available.

Examples Of Project Briefs

- Design and make an alarm system to protect a bicycle.

- Design and make an electronic device to select lotto numbers.

- Design and make an electronic device which will assist snooker or darts players when totalling their score.

- Design and make an electronic device to be worn by children walking at night or by joggers to make their presence known to motorists.

- Design and make an electronic money box which outputs a reward each time a child inserts a coin.

- Design and make an electronic die to replace a conventional die for use with a board game.

- Design and make an electronic system which will indicate to a caravan owner that the gas level in a gas bottle is getting low.

- Design and make an electronic aid to assist sports people with their training or to improve their skill.

An Alternative Approach

Your teacher may set a number of project themes for you to choose from. An example of a theme is given below.

'A small electronics company wishes to market a range of low-cost alarm systems. They intend to target these devices at particular potential customer groups and you have been asked to design and make a prototype device for the company.'

You can start this type of problem by identifying the different types of alarms the company could develop. Examples include:

Jewellery box alarm

Car alarm

Smoke alarm

Baby monitoring alarm

Look at alarms and try to find out what they all have in common. You will notice that the electronic components which make up an alarm circuit are very similar, whatever the purpose of the alarm.

You can use the theme as a starting point and then through investigation you can devise your own design brief based on your interests or needs.

You should begin by explaining the task you have chosen or the problem you hope to solve by designing and making your product. One way of doing this is to clearly explain the factors you need to consider when designing your electronic product.

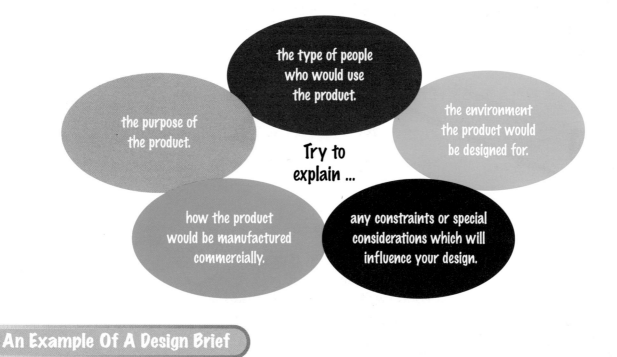

the type of people who would use the product.

the purpose of the product.

the environment the product would be designed for.

Try to explain ...

how the product would be manufactured commercially.

any constraints or special considerations which will influence your design.

An Example Of A Design Brief

The example below is for an alarm project.

Purpose Of Project

My grandparents like gardening and have a garden shed where they store all their gardening equipment. The shed has a single door which is protected by a lock and a window panel which cannot be opened. Although the shed is also protected by security lighting from the house, it has been broken into and tools have been stolen. The shed needs an alarm system which will be noisy to discourage thieves from staying in the shed if they break in.

Target Users

Although the shed alarm is intended for my grandparents, there is no reason why this product could not be made available to other people who have a garden shed or a garage.

Environment

In bad weather, the garden shed can become cold and damp. When it is windy, the door of the shed rattles in the door frame.

Constraints

The garden shed is not connected to mains electricity.

When analysing a problem you will need to consider the project in more detail and organise your thoughts. Start by breaking the problem down into a number of smaller problems or sub-systems. An Electronic Products project immediately divides into two parts: the electronics, and the case to package the electronic circuitry, battery and input and output devices.

Things To Consider

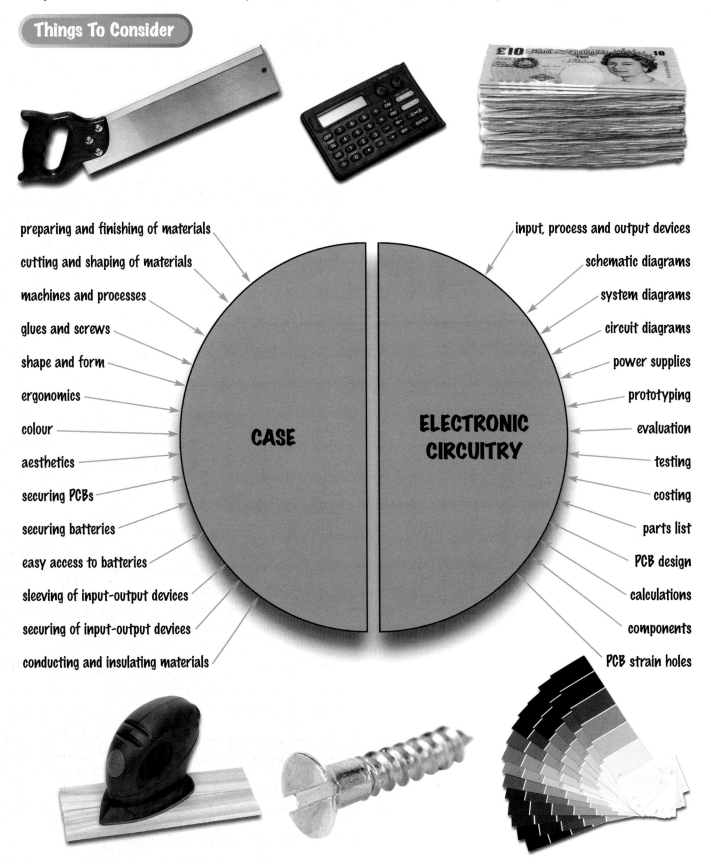

preparing and finishing of materials

cutting and shaping of materials

machines and processes

glues and screws

shape and form

ergonomics

colour

aesthetics

securing PCBs

securing batteries

easy access to batteries

sleeving of input-output devices

securing of input-output devices

conducting and insulating materials

CASE

ELECTRONIC CIRCUITRY

input, process and output devices

schematic diagrams

system diagrams

circuit diagrams

power supplies

prototyping

evaluation

testing

costing

parts list

PCB design

calculations

components

PCB strain holes

Ideally, you should list all of the tasks you may need to consider during the project. Remember you have been studying Design and Technology for several years and you already know a great deal. Put your thoughts on paper.

A good way of starting your analysis is to identify the input and output devices you could possibly use. The input to many alarm systems is often a sensing device. Look in the Rapid catalogue to see what you can find, or visit their website: www.rapideducation.co.uk

Analyse The Problem

Ask yourself questions about the parts of the product and try to find the answers. This table gives you an idea of the type of questions you might ask yourself.

Questions	*Answers*
What can I use as an arming switch to switch the system on and off?	*This could be a key switch or a key pad.*
What can I use as a triggering switch?	*This could be a tilt switch, proximity switch, micro switch, vibration switch, pressure pad or piezo transducer.*
What siren can I use that will operate from a DC power supply?	*There are a number of sirens in the Rapid catalogue with an operating voltage of 5V to 15V and a sound output of 105dB.*

Primary Research

Designing for a real client will often mean you have to carry out real primary research which will provide you with much more useful information.

For the shed alarm project, you could visit your grandparents' shed and make a rough sketch of its size and shape. If you have a camera, you could take photographs to include in your design folder.

Investigate the shed door and find out if it opens inwards or outwards. This may influence your choice of input switch.

Look at the door frame and identify where the input device could be fitted. Again, make sketches or take photographs.

Go into the shed and find a suitable place to fit the alarm box. Choose a place which is concealed, yet easy for your grandparents to get to.

An alarm for a garage may include the investigation of up-and-over doors. The garage may also have a side door and a window to protect.

Collecting Information Via Questionnaires

Great skill is required to produce good questionnaires. The questions should be unambiguous and not too open-ended. Choose questions carefully, and make sure there is nothing to offend different genders and cultures. Ideally, the questions ought to be answered by ticking one of a range of boxes. This enables the results to be analysed much more easily. However, sometimes this is impossible, especially if you are asking a fairly complex question. Questionnaires can be photocopied and handed out, but you may have to push people to get them to hand them back to you!

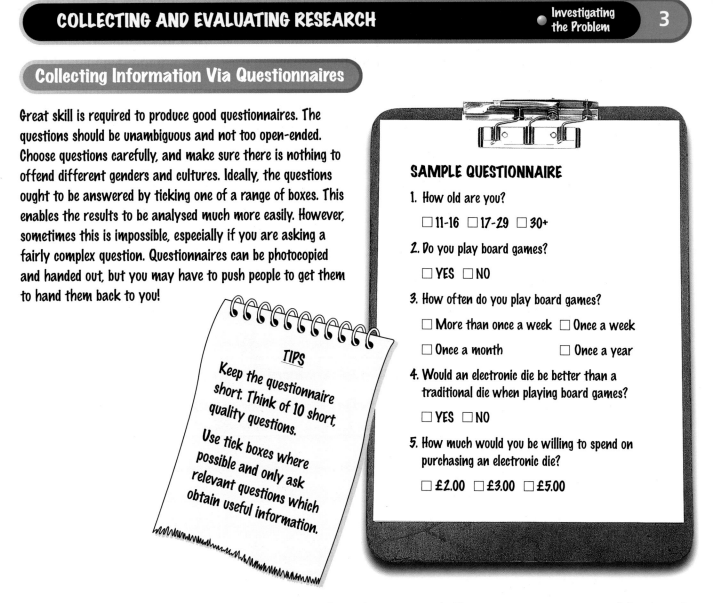

TIPS

Keep the questionnaire short. Think of 10 short, quality questions.

Use tick boxes where possible and only ask relevant questions which obtain useful information.

SAMPLE QUESTIONNAIRE

1. How old are you?
   ☐ 11-16 ☐ 17-29 ☐ 30+

2. Do you play board games?
   ☐ YES ☐ NO

3. How often do you play board games?
   ☐ More than once a week ☐ Once a week
   ☐ Once a month ☐ Once a year

4. Would an electronic die be better than a traditional die when playing board games?
   ☐ YES ☐ NO

5. How much would you be willing to spend on purchasing an electronic die?
   ☐ £2.00 ☐ £3.00 ☐ £5.00

Remember, asking ten people is unlikely to provide you with a valid survey result. You need to target your potential users and seek a good cross-section of opinions if your data is to be reliable. Once you have collated the results, you can produce line graphs, bar charts and pie charts.

Line Graphs	Bar Charts (Histograms)	Pie Charts
These are useful for showing changes over time. They are a set of dots (or crosses), with adjacent dots joined together by a straight line.	These are useful for making comparisons of results.	These are useful for representing information as a percentage to show clear comparisons.

Databases or spreadsheets can help you collate the results of your questionnaire and can generate useful graphs. It is essential to explain how the survey was carried out, what questions were asked and how the results influence your thinking.

Product analysis can be the most useful way of identifying the research you need to carry out. It involves looking carefully at a product, and investigating how it works and how it was made.

Opening a smoke alarm will show how the PCB, battery and input and output devices are fitted into the case. Unfortunately it will not show how the electronic components and integrated circuits work together to make an alarm circuit. This is the problem with disassembling an electronic product: you cannot see how the process section works.

A standard
smoke alarm

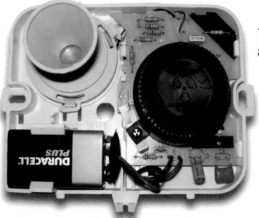

The insides of
a smoke alarm

You will therefore have to use your imagination to take apart the process section of the circuit by observing and recording what is taking place. For example, for the garden shed alarm project, you could investigate a house burglar alarm and make notes of what happens.

Observations Of A Burglar Alarm

- The alarm has an arming switch (on/off) on the case of the alarm. (Input)
- The alarm has a timed exit delay which can be adjusted to suit the user. (Process)
- The alarm has a triggering switch on the front door of the house. (Input)
- If triggered, the alarm latches and the siren stays on for 15 minutes or until it is reset. (Process)
- The alarm has a timed entry delay which can be adjusted to suit the user. (Process)
- The alarm has a strobe light and a siren in a box on the side of the house. (Output)
- The strobe light stays on until re-set. (Output)

Basic Block System Diagram

You can then use your observations to create a basic block system diagram like this one.

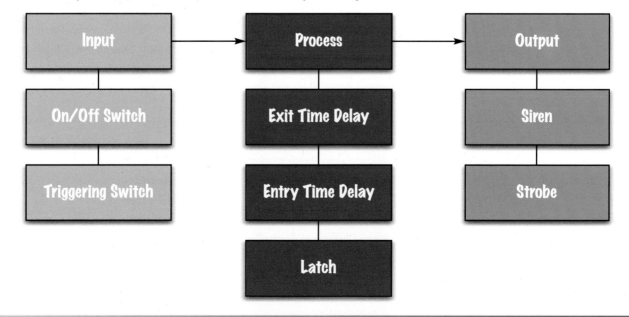

From your observations and analysis it is possible to construct a systems diagram for an alarm. If you start with the basic block system diagram you will see that as your ideas develop, so too will the block system diagram.

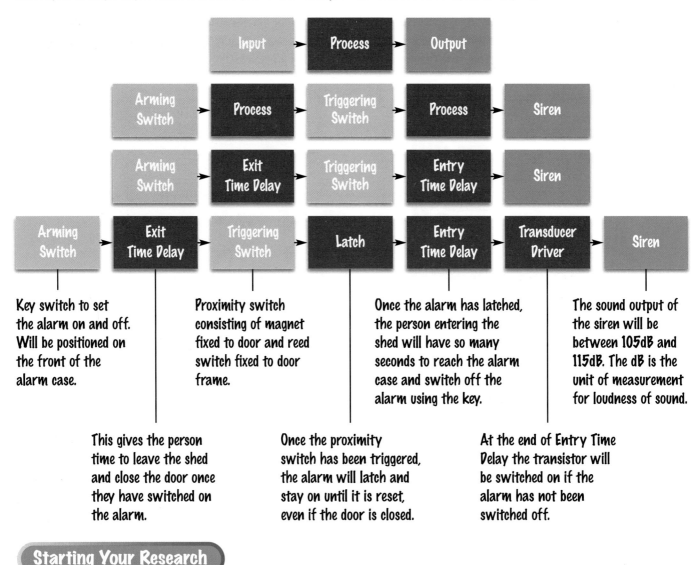

Key switch to set the alarm on and off. Will be positioned on the front of the alarm case.

Proximity switch consisting of magnet fixed to door and reed switch fixed to door frame.

Once the alarm has latched, the person entering the shed will have so many seconds to reach the alarm case and switch off the alarm using the key.

The sound output of the siren will be between 105dB and 115dB. The dB is the unit of measurement for loudness of sound.

This gives the person time to leave the shed and close the door once they have switched on the alarm.

Once the proximity switch has been triggered, the alarm will latch and stay on until it is reset, even if the door is closed.

At the end of Entry Time Delay the transistor will be switched on if the alarm has not been switched off.

Starting Your Research

When starting your research be guided by the information you have collected and developed through analysis and systems diagrams. Do not include in your research any material which does not inform the development of your ideas. Always question why you are including something in your folder. Remember, design folders should represent about 13 hours of work and it is quality that earns marks, not quantity.

The developed systems diagram above shows that the process sections of the alarm includes two time delays, a latch and a transducer driver. Start your research by making a list of electronic components and integrated circuits that could be used to make a monostable time delay, a latch and a transducer driver. Here are some examples of components that can be used ...

... to make a monostable time delay.	... to make a latch.	... as a transducer driver.
• 555 IC • Transistor • 4047 IC • Logic Integrated Circuit • Peripheral Interface Controller (PIC)	• Thyristor • Relay • Logic Integrated Circuit • Peripheral Interface Controller (PIC)	• Transistor • Field Effect Transistor (FET) • Thyristor • Relay

Explain Your Choices To The Moderator

In your design folder you should give reasons why you chose a certain way of making a monostable, latch and transducer driver and rejected the other methods. Reasons could be cost, size, working parameters of components or availability. Here is an explanation for the garden shed alarm project.

Selecting The Arming Switch
- A key switch will give security and is relatively cheap.

Selecting The Process Sections
- The two monostable time delays and the latch can be made using a single logic integrated circuit or a PIC.
- As the alarm has one triggering input and one output siren, a good choice economically is to use a 4011 IC which is a quad two-input NAND gate.
- If your alarm has a number of inputs and outputs, the better choice would be to use a PIC.
- Buying a PIC is more expensive than buying a logic IC. The PIC would also have to be programmed.

Selecting The Trigger Switch
- When it is windy, the door of the shed rattles in its frame and would set off the alarm if a vibration switch or a piezo transducer was used.
- A pressure pad on the floor of the shed would get dirty and damp and would have to be hidden by a mat.
- Micro switches would not be suitable as the shed door opens outwards.
- A proximity switch consists of a magnet and a reed switch moulded into a circular plastic package. This appears to be the most suitable switch. Find out if it is a normally open or normally closed switch. This may affect the design of the circuit in some way.

Selecting The Transducer Driver
- The output from a logic IC and a PIC is not powerful enough to drive a siren. Therefore, you will have to identify and select a suitable transducer driver.
- The simplest and most appropriate device to use is a transistor such as the BC639.

Your knowledge and understanding of your chosen final circuit will be more informed because you will have been active in selecting and rejecting various electronic sub-systems as your circuit evolves. Once you have chosen the sub-systems to make the circuit, carry out practical research by testing circuit ideas using kits, prototyping boards and computer simulation.

Summarise Your Research

Arming Switch	Exit Time Delay	Triggering Switch	Latch	Entry Time Delay	Transducer Driver	Siren
Key Switch	Quad Two-Input NAND Gate 4011 IC	Proximity Switch	Quad Two-Input NAND Gate 4011 IC	Quad Two-Input NAND Gate 4011 IC	NPN Transistor BC639	5V to 15V DC, 105dB to 115dB

Your research may now be leading you into the generation of ideas and you should have enough information to be able to start to construct a specification. Your specification should provide a detailed description of what the electronic product is to be. It should reflect the information found in your analysis and research and the conclusions and decisions you arrived at. It may well be that the specification is modified or updated a number of times as you proceed with the designing.

Below is an example of what you could include in your specification.

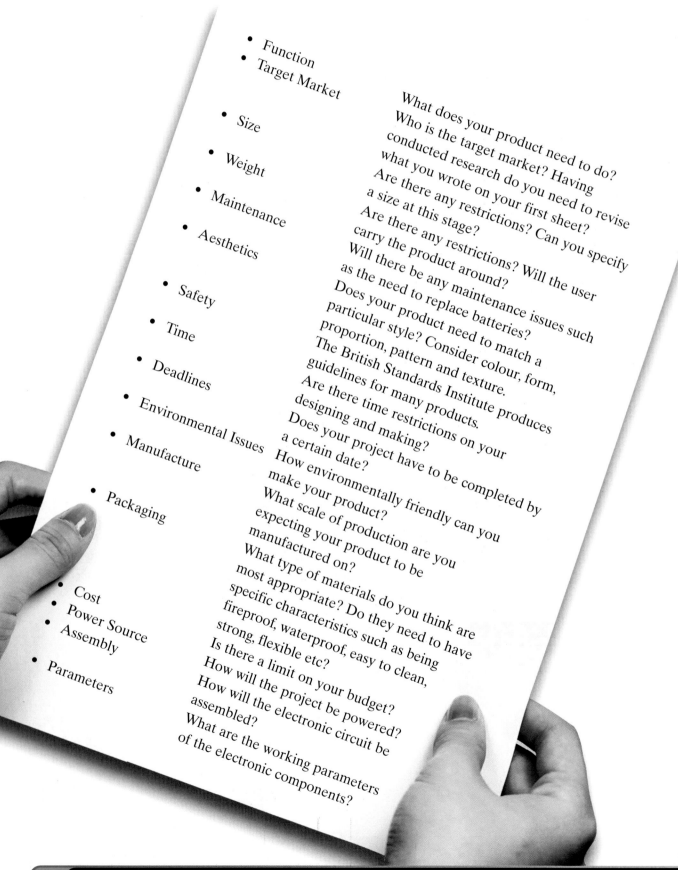

- Function — What does your product need to do?
- Target Market — Who is the target market? Having conducted research do you need to revise what you wrote on your first sheet?
- Size — Are there any restrictions? Can you specify a size at this stage?
- Weight — Are there any restrictions? Will the user carry the product around?
- Maintenance — Will there be any maintenance issues such as the need to replace batteries?
- Aesthetics — Does your product need to match a particular style? Consider colour, form, proportion, pattern and texture.
- Safety — The British Standards Institute produces guidelines for many products.
- Time — Are there time restrictions on your designing and making?
- Deadlines — Does your project have to be completed by a certain date?
- Environmental Issues — How environmentally friendly can you make your product?
- Manufacture — What scale of production are you expecting your product to be manufactured on?
- Packaging — What type of materials do you think are most appropriate? Do they need to have specific characteristics such as being fireproof, waterproof, easy to clean, strong, flexible etc?
- Cost — Is there a limit on your budget?
- Power Source — How will the project be powered?
- Assembly — How will the electronic circuit be assembled?
- Parameters — What are the working parameters of the electronic components?

A good specification is crucial to the success of any Electronic Products project and will make it easier for you to carry out ongoing and final evaluation. You will be expected to test and evaluate the product in the environment it was designed for to see whether it will meet the demands of the criteria.

An Example Of An Alarm Specification

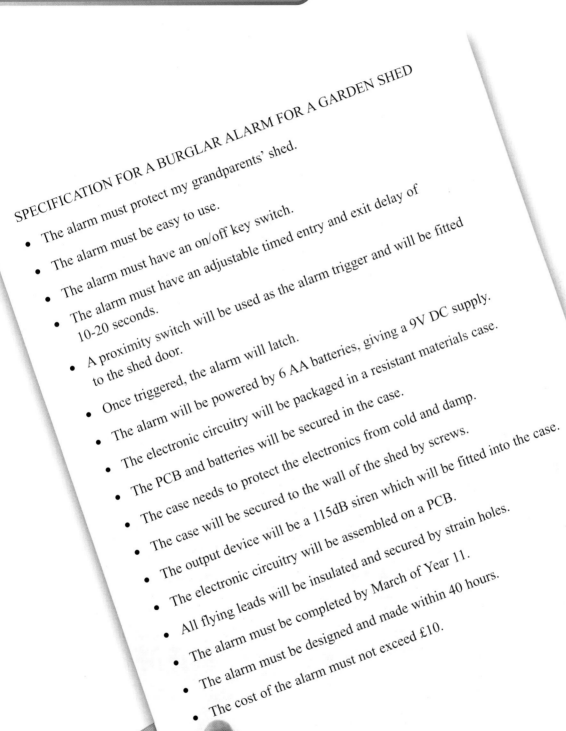

SPECIFICATION FOR A BURGLAR ALARM FOR A GARDEN SHED

- The alarm must protect my grandparents' shed.
- The alarm must be easy to use.
- The alarm must have an on/off key switch.
- The alarm must have an adjustable timed entry and exit delay of 10-20 seconds.
- A proximity switch will be used as the alarm trigger and will be fitted to the shed door.
- Once triggered, the alarm will latch.
- The alarm will be powered by 6 AA batteries, giving a 9V DC supply.
- The electronic circuitry will be packaged in a resistant materials case.
- The PCB and batteries will be secured in the case.
- The case needs to protect the electronics from cold and damp.
- The case will be secured to the wall of the shed by screws.
- The output device will be a 115dB siren which will be fitted into the case.
- The electronic circuitry will be assembled on a PCB.
- All flying leads will be insulated and secured by strain holes.
- The alarm must be completed by March of Year 11.
- The alarm must be designed and made within 40 hours.
- The cost of the alarm must not exceed £10.

You need to gather and explore circuits from any suitable resources. This can include material from books, data sheets, computer-generated information and circuit ideas supplied by your teacher.

Case And Electronic Circuit Ideas

As a general guide, you should produce three electronic circuit ideas and two ideas for a case to be made of suitable resistant materials.

Case ideas should be relatively simple and appropriate to house an electronic circuit. At GCSE level, Awarding Bodies do not expect you to design original electronic circuits, but rather to select and modify existing circuits to meet your project's needs. This may involve you finding a way of joining together two separate circuits or changing the input and output devices, or finding a different way of latching, or completely re-designing a circuit to fit into a small space. As your work develops, you can try out your ideas by building circuits on prototyping board or by computer circuit simulation. You should use and become familiar with measuring instruments and check your results against mathematical calculations.

Organisation Of Your Design Folder

If your design folder is to be completed in 13 hours, parts of your analysis and research must contribute towards the generation of ideas.

Make sure you use notes to guide the moderator to sections of your design folder which make a wider contribution to the assessment criteria.

Parts of your analysis, research and generation of ideas will naturally overlap. It is sometimes difficult to see where one section starts and another section finishes. Do not worry about this - this is the nature of designing. Once again, let your generation of ideas be guided by the analysis and research you have already carried out. Parts of your research will certainly qualify as generation of ideas if you have considered a number of different ways of making electronic sub-systems.

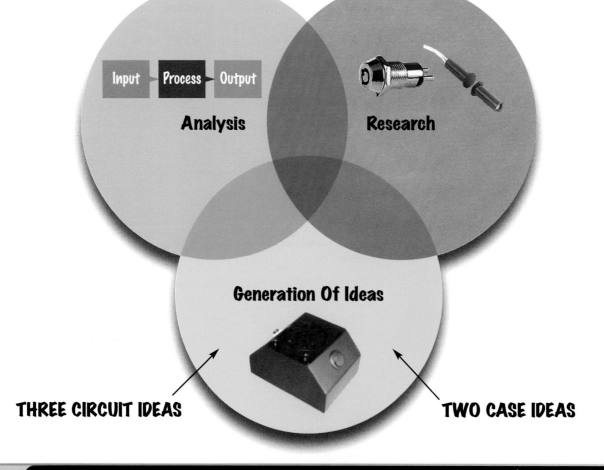

THREE CIRCUIT IDEAS   TWO CASE IDEAS

Present your design ideas by using a range of traditional and computer-aided graphical techniques in a way that can be clearly understood by the moderator. To complete the design folder within the suggested time scale of 13 hours will mean that you have to make good use of ICT.

Paper Size - A3 Or A4?

Whatever size of paper you are using for your design folder, whether it is A3 or A4, remember to make maximum use of each sheet. The best ideas sheets are those which are busy with lots of circuit diagrams and drawings of cases accompanied with notes. If you are using A3 paper, you could paste ideas from several smaller sheets together to make an interesting design arrangement. This works particularly well when designing for your case. The sheet could include your two case designs showing how the PCB and the battery or individual cells are fitted and secured in the case, and the position of the switch and input/output devices.

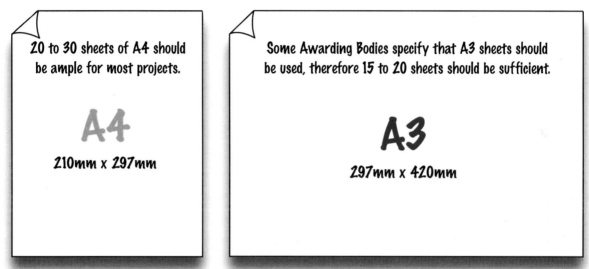

20 to 30 sheets of A4 should be ample for most projects.

A4
210mm x 297mm

Some Awarding Bodies specify that A3 sheets should be used, therefore 15 to 20 sheets should be sufficient.

A3
297mm x 420mm

You will need to organise your design folder carefully. Do not waste time drawing elaborate borders, titles and logos. Use ICT to help you, and remember it is the quality of the content that gains the marks.

Computer-Aided Design (CAD)

Using a CAD system will make it quicker and easier for you to create a design for your circuit or case than using traditional drawing and modelling methods. Crocodile Technology and Livewire are two electronic circuit simulator software design packages which enable you to model electronic circuits and to explore their behaviour without needing to build them from real components. Ask your teacher if your school has a software licence to allow you to take copies home to work with.

The circuit diagrams produced using Crocodile Technology or Livewire can be directly imported into PCB Wizard 3 or Real-PCB which are software packages that can be used to design PCBs. Both design packages contain a library of tracks, pads and components and allow you to be fully involved in the design of your PCB.

Pro/DESKTOP is a software package which you can use to design cases to house your electronic circuitry and battery. Case designs can be quickly generated and rendered to suit the materials being used.

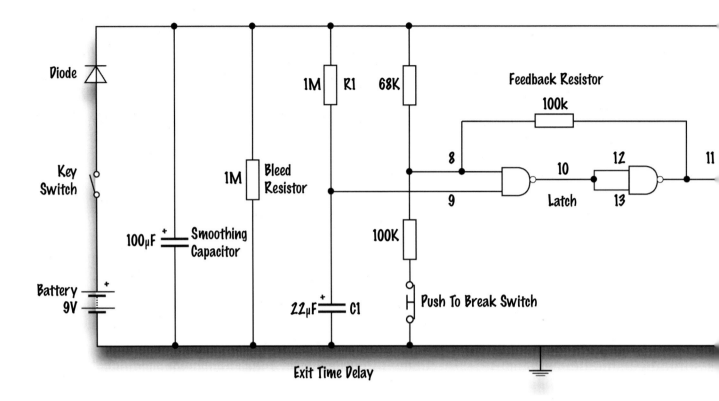

Exit Time Delay

You should present an accurate final circuit diagram which satisfies the specification and clearly takes into account relevant research and analysis. The circuit diagram should contain sufficient information for the circuit to be made by a competent third person. If you have already done this, make sure the moderator knows where to find it. Above is an example of a circuit design for an alarm circuit with exit and entry time delays. The logic alarm is triggered by break contacts.

How The Circuit Works

- **WHEN THE KEY SWITCH IS CLOSED,** the alarm circuit is connected to the 9V PP3 battery.
- The diode in series with the key switch protects the circuit against the possibility of the battery being incorrectly connected with regards to polarity.
- As the key switch is closed, C1, the 22µF capacitor, immediately starts to charge up through R1, the 1M fixed resistor.
- When the voltage across C1 reaches approximately 8V, pin 9 goes high.
- Pin 8 is being held at a voltage of 3.5V by the potential divider network formed by the 68K fixed resistor and the 100K fixed resistor.
- When operating a CMOS logic IC from a 9V battery, the low or logic 0 is in the voltage range 0V to 2V. The high or logic 1 is in the voltage range 8V to 9V.
- The input voltage that is used to change the logic level is called the THRESHOLD voltage. Therefore a CMOS logic IC with a voltage of 3.5V on one of its input pins will result in that pin being in a state which is neither high nor low, but will operate logically as a low due to the voltage being less than 8V.
- Pin 8 is low and pin 9 is high, therefore pin 10 will be high.

NAND Gate Truth Table

A (Pin 8)	B (Pin 9)	Q (Pin 10)
0	0	1
0	1	1
1	0	1
1	1	0

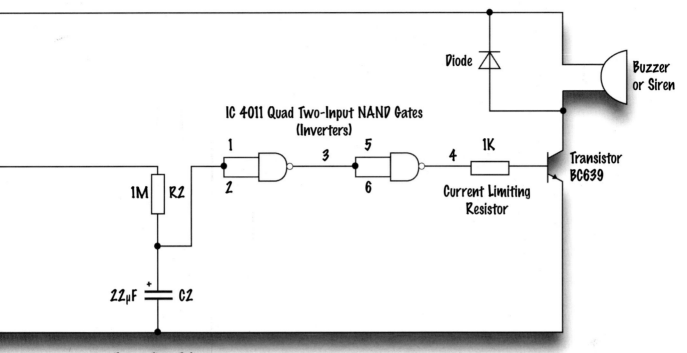

Entry Time Delay

- Pins 12 and 13 are connected together and therefore the NAND gate becomes a NOT gate or an INVERTER.
- If pin 10 is high, pins 12 and 13 will also be high and the inverter makes the output at pin 11 low.
- The low output at pin 11 is fed back to pin 8 through the 100K feedback resistor.
- **WHEN THE PTB SWITCH IS PRESSED,** the voltage input to pin 8 goes high. So pins 8 and 9 are both high, making pin 10 low.
- With pin 10 low, pins 12 and 13 are also low.
- The inverter makes pin 11 high and this high is fed back to pin 8 through the 100K feedback resistor.
- Although the PTB switch has returned to closed state and pin 8 is no longer directly connected to the positive supply rail, pin 8 remains high through the feedback resistor. The system has LATCHED.
- With pin 11 high, C2, the 22μF capacitor, charges up through R2, the 1M fixed resistor.
- When C2 reaches approximately 8V, pins 1 and 2, which are connected together, go high.
- The high on pins 1 and 2 is inverted to a low on pin 3.
- The low on pin 3 means that pins 5 and 6 are also low.
- With pins 5 and 6 connected together, the low is inverted to a high on pin 4.
- The 1K fixed resistor protects the transducer driver by limiting the current to the base of the transistor.
- The diode across the siren protects the transistor from back electromotive force (emf) when the transistor switches off.

Also ...

- The 1M bleed resistor provides a discharge path for C1, the 22μF capacitor. So C1 will discharge through two 1M fixed resistors.
- The 100μF smoothing capacitor provides a stabilising condition across the circuit, resulting in no loss of voltage across the power rails, especially when the siren is sounding.
- The exit and entry time delays can be made adjustable by changing R1 and R2 from fixed resistors to 1M potentiometers (variable resistors).
- Digital switching is achieved by the last two NAND gates connected as inverters. When the voltage across C2 reaches 8V, the transistor is switched on.
- With CMOS logic ICs, all unused input pins must be connected to plus volts (+V) or zero volts (0V). They must not be left unconnected.
- The four NAND gates in the circuit above are packaged in a quad 2-input IC (see page 103).

Designing Your PCB

1 Make sure you have modelled or tested your chosen electronic circuit to check that it works before you start to design the PCB layout. You could use Crocodile Technology or Livewire for computer simulation of the circuit, or use a prototyping board with real components.

2 Check the size of the components to determine how much space they require and the best location for them on the PCB. Measure the size of, and distance between, the pins, leads and connections of the components you intend to use. The distance between the pin connections for ICs is 0.1 inch.

3 Carefully study the outputs and inputs of each IC. If you are using more than one IC, spend time looking at the relationship between the ICs and position them on the PCB in a way that simplifies the track layout. Remember - there are four ways of placing an IC on a PCB...

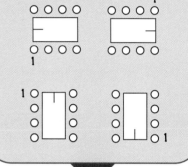

7 Remember that the PCB has a component side and a track side. You may have to flip your design through 180° before you print it onto acetate sheet. Check this with your teacher.

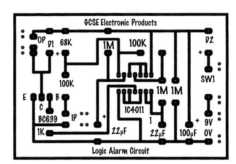

6 Make the pads big enough - making the pads too small with a large hole in the centre will make it extremely difficult for you to achieve a good soldered joint. Make your tracks wide enough - narrow tracks can easily be damaged by the ferric chloride solution in the etching tank or by other processes.

5 Draw the components to their approximate size on graph paper with a 0.1 inch grid. Use vertical and horizontal tracks so that the components will be at right angles to each other.

4 Carefully plan the position of the components for the PCB design. Make the design big enough to give you enough space to position the components and solder them in place. Marks will not be deducted due to the size of the PCB.

For many pupils of Electronic Products, this part of the design process means the development of a PCB layout from the circuit diagram. Whatever type of component assembly board you intend to use, you should show evidence that you have planned the layout of the circuit to make it as easy as possible to assemble and solder the components, position the input and output devices, secure the circuit board into the case and inspect the circuit. If Veroboard is used, you should show recorded evidence in your design folder of planning the component layout, the number of link wires required and the position of the breaks in the conductive tracks. If you intend to use a PCB, it is good practice to show the design development of the PCB. Therefore, print out copies of the PCB as you develop it. All mistakes, corrections and modifications should be indicated on the printouts.

Computer-Aided Manufacture

Awarding Bodies will accept your PCB mask as evidence of a basic form of Computer-Aided Manufacture. The PCB mask is designed on a computer and then copied onto acetate sheet using a laser printer. The mask is then placed in a light box and can be used repeatedly to manufacture identical PCBs.

If your project is to achieve a high grade, it is very important that you have a PCB of quality. Spend time developing it, making sure there are no errors before you use it. Remember: any mistakes on the mask will be transferred to your PCB. The production of a PCB mask will also gain you designing and making marks.

You need to explain why you chose to develop a particular idea for your case. Therefore, give reasons why you selected a certain case design from your generation of ideas, and explain why you rejected the others.

You should present an accurate final drawing that contains enough information to enable a competent third person to construct the case.

An Example Of A Case Design

This case design for a shed alarm has been produced with the use of Pro/DESKTOP.

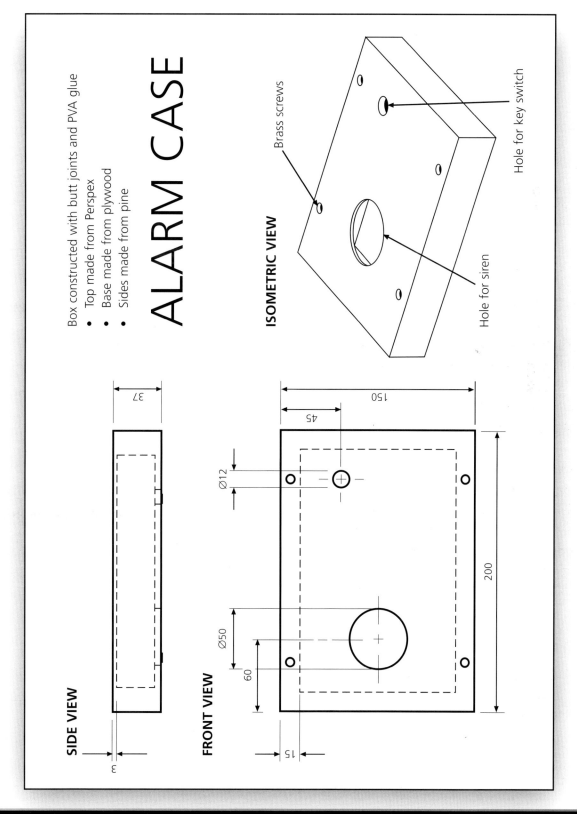

ALARM CASE

Box constructed with butt joints and PVA glue
- Top made from Perspex
- Base made from plywood
- Sides made from pine

ISOMETRIC VIEW

Brass screws

Hole for key switch

Hole for siren

SIDE VIEW

FRONT VIEW

Ø12
Ø50
60
15
45
150
200
37
3

How To Make A PCB By The Photographic Method

You will have already developed the design for your PCB. The step-by-step process below shows you how to produce your PCB using the photographic method. For more information on the initial stages of the process, refer to pages 25 and 28.

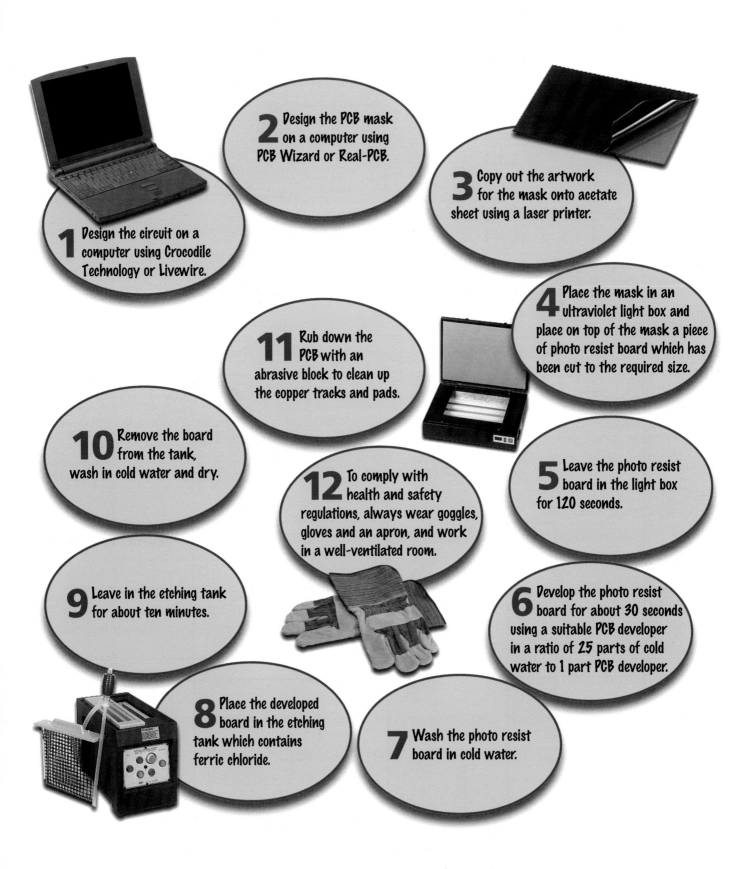

1 Design the circuit on a computer using Crocodile Technology or Livewire.

2 Design the PCB mask on a computer using PCB Wizard or Real-PCB.

3 Copy out the artwork for the mask onto acetate sheet using a laser printer.

4 Place the mask in an ultraviolet light box and place on top of the mask a piece of photo resist board which has been cut to the required size.

5 Leave the photo resist board in the light box for 120 seconds.

6 Develop the photo resist board for about 30 seconds using a suitable PCB developer in a ratio of 25 parts of cold water to 1 part PCB developer.

7 Wash the photo resist board in cold water.

8 Place the developed board in the etching tank which contains ferric chloride.

9 Leave in the etching tank for about ten minutes.

10 Remove the board from the tank, wash in cold water and dry.

11 Rub down the PCB with an abrasive block to clean up the copper tracks and pads.

12 To comply with health and safety regulations, always wear goggles, gloves and an apron, and work in a well-ventilated room.

Quality Control

Once the PCB has been made, carry out an inspection of it by looking for breaks in the tracks, missing pads and bridging across tracks and pads. Look very carefully at the IC socket pads which are only 0.1 inches apart. A magnifying glass can be very useful when carrying out this type of work.

If a track looks as though it has a hairline break in it, check the continuity of the track by using a multimeter set on the OHMS range.

Drilling The PCB

Once you are satisfied that you have produced a quality PCB, carefully drill all the pads of the PCB using a 1mm diameter drill. Extra care and attention is required when drilling the pads for ICs. Goggles should be worn, ties tucked into shirts and long hair tied back.

Quality Assurance

To secure the battery and other devices attached to flying leads, drill two 2mm diameter strain holes around each relevant pad on the PCB and thread the leads through the holes. The strain holes will help stop the flying leads being pulled out of the soldered joint. This type of attention to detail is an example of building quality assurance into your product.

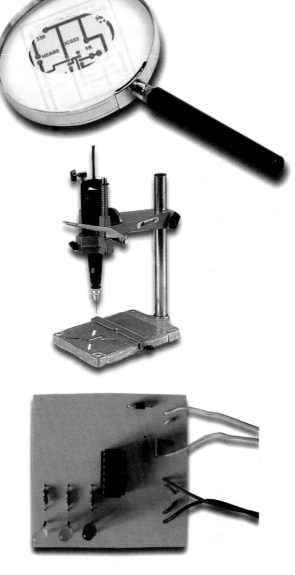

Populating The PCB

Most PCBs produced in schools are single sided with holes drilled through the PCB for component location. This means that the components are placed on the opposite side to the copper tracks and pushed as close as possible to the PCB.

Before populating a PCB with electronic components, carefully bend the leads of the components using small pliers to make them fit into the gap between their respective pads. The leads of polar components can be insulated in red or black sleeving to indicate polarity. This will help you when placing the components onto the PCB and when carrying out testing or fault finding.

Start by attaching the low profile components, such as resistors and diodes, then add taller components as the circuit progresses. Leave sensitive components, such as transistors, until the end and always use IC sockets.

Soldering

Check that the soldering iron is hot enough to melt the solder by applying solder to the tip of the iron. Clean the tip of the soldering iron by wiping it on a damp sponge. Place the soldering iron against the copper pad and the lead of the component to be soldered. Hold the soldering iron there for 2 to 3 seconds then place the solder on the pad and against the lead and allow the solder to flow onto the pad. The soldering iron and the solder should not come into contact. The heat required to melt the solder should come from the copper pad and the component lead. This technique will ensure that the soldering temperatures of the copper pad, component lead and solder are all similar and will help to eliminate dry joints. To complete the process, snip away any unwanted pieces of wire.

How To Make The Case For A Shed Alarm – An Example

Shown below as an example are the manufacturing stages for constructing a case for a shed alarm, using plywood, pine and Perspex. Depending on the type of case you intend to make, the stages will differ accordingly. Write down the stages in the process that you will use to make your case. If you intend to vacuum form a case, do not forget to show the stages for making the former. Keep the former for moderation purposes.

1 Design the case by traditional drawing methods or use a software package such as Pro/DESKTOP.

2 Make a fully dimensioned working drawing taking into account the size of the PCB, battery, switches and siren.

3 The case will be made from pine. Mark out all the required parts.

4 Cut and shape the parts to the required sizes using appropriate machine and hand tools.

5 Drill and counterbore the case for switches and any other devices.

6 Sand down all parts.

7 Glue case together holding it in place with clamps or a vice.

8 Make the sides of the case flush on a disc sanding machine.

9 Cut a piece of plywood to fit the back of the case, and glue it to the case.

10 Cut a piece of Perspex to fit the front of the case, drill holes for brass wood screws, key switch and siren.

11 Check all the pieces fit together.

12 Assemble the case with the Perspex panel screwed in place.

13 Rub down with fine glass paper.

14 Polish edges of Perspex panels.

15 Varnish and carry out your final inspection.

An important part of planning the making of an electronic product is the component parts list. Always make sure the components you need are available and within your project costs. Look in the Rapid Electronics catalogue and become familiar with the data needed to order components. You will immediately notice that the more components you buy, the cheaper they are. Discuss this with your teacher. Your school may have an account with a components supplier to enable a bulk order to be made. On the written examination paper, there are sometimes questions on using component data sheets and applying the information.

Here is an example of a components and cost list for an alarm circuit with exit and entry time delays with a logic alarm that is triggered by break contacts.

Component List

QUANTITY	DESCRIPTION	ORDER NUMBER	COST PER ITEM
2	Terminal Blocks	21-0450	10p
1	PP3 Battery Clip	18-0105	3p
1	Miniature Key Switch	79-0295	160p
2	IN4001 Diode	47-3130	1p
3	1M Resistor	62-0445	1p
2	100K Resistor	62-0421	1p
1	68K Resistor	62-0417	1p
1	1K Resistor	62-0373	1p
2	22μF Capacitor	11-0230	2p
1	100μF Capacitor	11-0245	3p
1	4011 NAND IC	83-0328	11p
1	14 Pin IC Socket	22-0155	5p
1	BC639 Transistor	81-0080	5p
1	Economy Photo etch PCB	34-0176	75p
	INPUT DEVICE		
1	Proximity Switch	78-0797	98p
	OUTPUT DEVICE		
1	Small Siren available from: Maplin Electronics Freepost NEA 9437 Barnsley. S73 0BR	YD76H	425p

All components are available from: Rapid Electronics Limited
Severalls Lane
Colchester
Essex
CO4 5JS

Telephone: 01206 751166

Ongoing Evaluation

The moderator will expect to see in your design folder evidence of the evaluation and testing which you have undertaken at regular intervals throughout your project. There should also be a final evaluation which summarises what you have done, how successful your project appears to be and what modifications you would make if you had to produce your project in batch quantities of, for example, 30.

Testing

Testing your product is an important part of your evaluation and will highlight any changes that may be needed. Companies that make electronic products carry out numerous tests before a product goes into full-scale production. Try to think up interesting ways of testing your product in the environmental conditions it was designed for. Record your results in your design folder using block diagrams or pie charts. As well as recording people's comments and opinions, try to obtain data that can be measured and compared. Once again, photography can be used to record evidence of testing and to identify any modifications that are needed to improve the product.

Did you find the product easy to use?

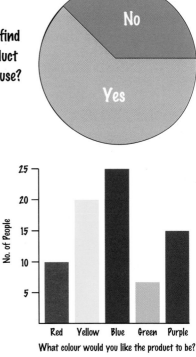

What colour would you like the product to be?

Final Evaluation

Your final evaluation should include a review of your product operating in the environmental conditions it was designed for, and comments on whether or not it meets the demands of the specification. A good place to start would be to ask yourself the following questions:

- Do you find the product easy to use?
- Does it function in the way it was intended to?
- What do you think about the style of the product?
- Do you like or dislike any features? Explain why.
- Would you purchase this product and, if so, what would you expect to pay for such a product?
- What are its main advantages and disadvantages compared to similar products?

As well as using your own judgement you can use the judgements of clients to assess your product's success. Asking the opinion of other people is an important part of evaluation.

The final evaluation is one of the few places in a design folder that gives you the chance to carry out an extended piece of writing. Remember there are 5 marks available for the quality of your written communication.

Specification

You should test your product against the original specification. Check your prototype against each of the criteria you originally listed. Was the design specification correct? Did you need to revise this as the work progressed? A simple chart might help.

SPECIFICATION CRITERIA	TEST OR QUESTION	RESULTS AND EXPLANATIONS
The alarm must be easy to use.	Could the alarm be switched on and off in the entry and exit time delay?	During daylight, yes, but in darkness there was a problem and a torch was needed.
The alarm must have a siren.	Will it deter burglars who break into the garden shed?	In the shed, the loudness of the siren is painful on the ears, and the siren can be heard from inside the house.

Modifications Needed

There is no such thing as the perfect design. All products can be improved. Despite all the time and effort you have put into designing and making your prototype, there will be some scope for improvements.

The first thing to do is to respond to the tests and to other people's comments. Issues such as colour are not usually very important and nothing other than a comment from you is required. If there are major problems with your design then you will need to respond in more detail.

Major problems do not mean that you will gain a low grade. You could still get a high grade even if your electronic product does not fully work as intended. It is quite possible that some students will have difficulty in getting their electronic circuits to work and will need to make suggestions for improvements and have evidence to show the moderator that they have carried out tests and tried to correct any errors or mistakes. It is the process of design that is being assessed, and therefore problems with your circuit can be an opportunity for you to achieve highly on evaluation, testing and modifications. You will need to ensure that you allow enough time for a full evaluation to take place - many students do not. Design work at this stage will be assessed under several headings, so it really is valuable to your overall grade.

Modifications For Production

This is also an area you will need to address. The first thing to do is to arrange a meeting with a real expert (yes, your teacher!). They should be able to assist you with some of the answers. Make suggestions about the processes which might be used if your design was commercially produced. Comments such as 'I would use CAD/CAM' will gain you no credit. You will need to explain your industrial understanding.

Ask yourself the following questions:

- Would they use the materials that I used in my prototype?
- Would the construction methods be the same?
- How would the surface finishes differ from my prototype?
- Can I make design changes which would reduce production costs?
- Is there scope for automating parts of the manufacturing process?
- Can I reduce the number of different components in my design?

A production manager would certainly be looking at these issues and would also be thinking about the production aids which would be needed. Can you think of any aids, such as jigs, templates and fixtures, which would help you if you had to produce 30 identical electronic products?

Freehand Sketching

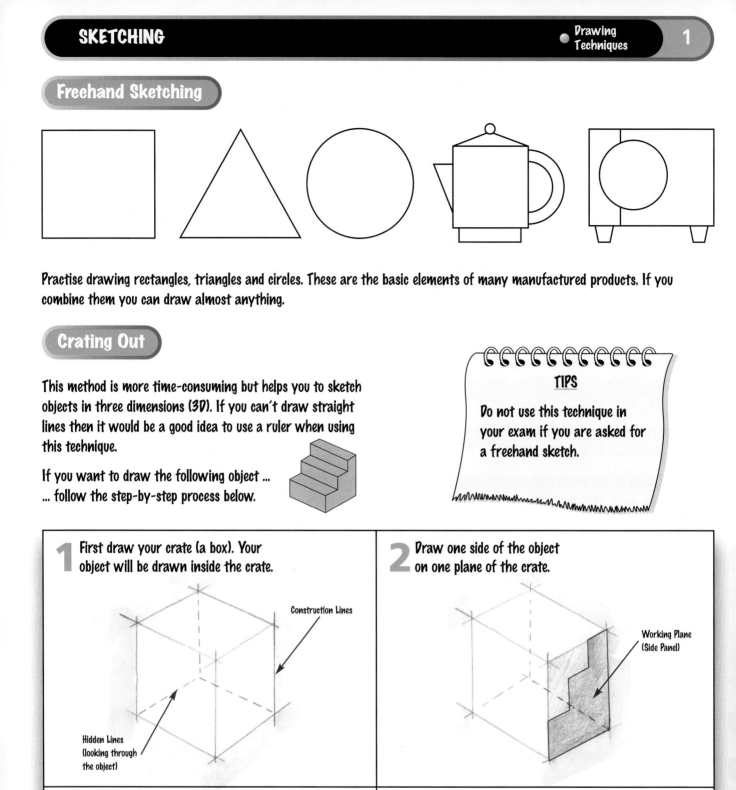

Practise drawing rectangles, triangles and circles. These are the basic elements of many manufactured products. If you combine them you can draw almost anything.

Crating Out

This method is more time-consuming but helps you to sketch objects in three dimensions (3D). If you can't draw straight lines then it would be a good idea to use a ruler when using this technique.

If you want to draw the following object ...
... follow the step-by-step process below.

TIPS

Do not use this technique in your exam if you are asked for a freehand sketch.

1 First draw your crate (a box). Your object will be drawn inside the crate.

Construction Lines

Hidden Lines (looking through the object)

2 Draw one side of the object on one plane of the crate.

Working Plane (Side Panel)

3 Copy the shape on the side panel onto the opposite plane of the crate.

TIPS
Leave the crate lines on - it shows the examiner how you have worked out your drawing.

4 Complete the sketch by drawing lines across from one plane to the other.

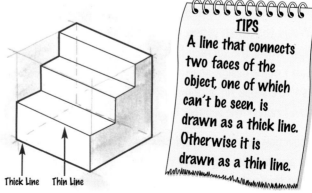

Thick Line   Thin Line

TIPS
A line that connects two faces of the object, one of which can't be seen, is drawn as a thick line. Otherwise it is drawn as a thin line.

Isometric projection is a drawing technique which looks fairly realistic and is commonly used to represent 3D objects. Its main advantage is that you can draw a 3D object to scale. The following stages show how you can draw a simple cube in isometric.

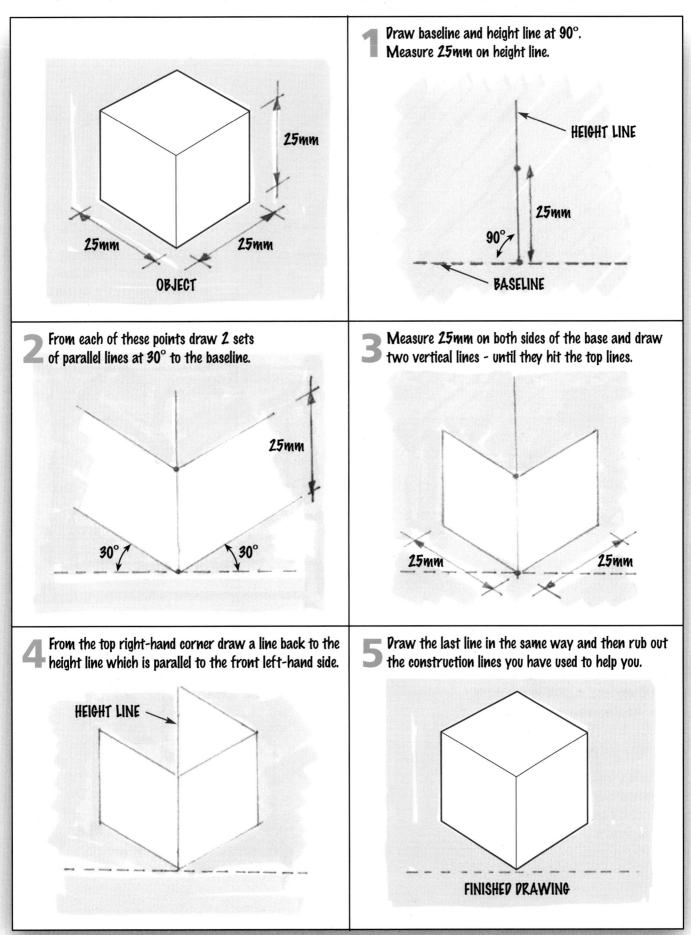

1 Draw baseline and height line at 90°. Measure 25mm on height line.

25mm

HEIGHT LINE

25mm

90°

BASELINE

OBJECT

25mm

25mm

25mm

2 From each of these points draw 2 sets of parallel lines at 30° to the baseline.

25mm

30°   30°

3 Measure 25mm on both sides of the base and draw two vertical lines - until they hit the top lines.

25mm   25mm

4 From the top right-hand corner draw a line back to the height line which is parallel to the front left-hand side.

HEIGHT LINE

5 Draw the last line in the same way and then rub out the construction lines you have used to help you.

FINISHED DRAWING

Drawing Circles In Isometric

Circles in isometric appear as ellipses, and by far the easiest way of drawing them is to use an ellipse template. However, it isn't too difficult to produce them freehand by following the instructions below.

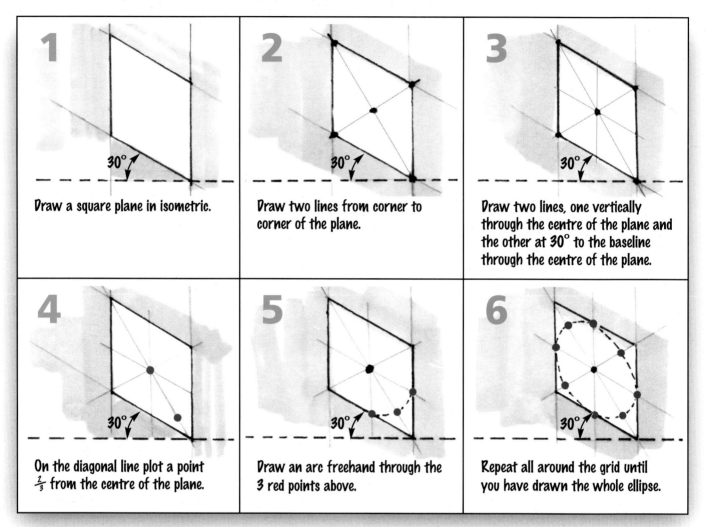

1
Draw a square plane in isometric.

2
Draw two lines from corner to corner of the plane.

3
Draw two lines, one vertically through the centre of the plane and the other at 30° to the baseline through the centre of the plane.

4
On the diagonal line plot a point $\frac{2}{3}$ from the centre of the plane.

5
Draw an arc freehand through the 3 red points above.

6
Repeat all around the grid until you have drawn the whole ellipse.

Exploded Drawings

Exploded drawings are used to show how objects fit together. Designers and architects use this method as it is quicker than drawing in perspective and helps them visualise what the object looks like and how it functions.

Opposite is a picture of a pencil sharpener, drawn as an exploded isometric. The construction lines are left in to show how it has been drawn.

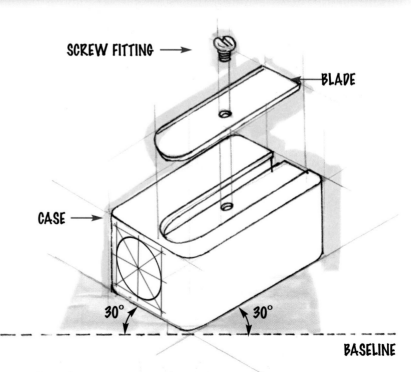

SCREW FITTING →

BLADE

CASE →

30°   30°

BASELINE

The designer will give a detailed drawing of the product to a manufacturer or model-maker. The drawings give the necessary instructions for a prototype to be built. Each drawing produced should include the following:

- accurate dimensions
- assembly instructions
- specification list of materials, colours and finishes.

Standards In Working Drawings

The British Standards Institution (BSI) has set standards in working drawings that are recognised throughout industry. Here are some examples of the basic standards required for your GCSE coursework.

1 LINES

Continuous thick line	For outlines or edges where only one of the faces forming an edge can be seen (could use an H or a 2H pencil)
Continuous thin line	For projection or dimension lines (could use a 4H pencil)
Chain thin line	For centre lines or lines of symmetry

2 DIMENSIONING

Interrupted View/Part View

Small Gap

Projection Line

Dimension in millimetres

16

Termination Arrowhead

30

Ø10 Dimensioning a Diameter

Dimension Line

Always use millimetres to dimension your drawing and write the number only - this is the recognised measurement for industrial drawings.

Numbers are always written above and in the middle of the dimension line - with all vertical dimensions written to the left of the dimension line. (These are always read from the right-hand side of the drawing.)

3 THIRD-ANGLE ORTHOGRAPHIC PROJECTION

This is the most common way of showing a working drawing. It is an accurate scale drawing of a product.

4 SCALE   FULL SIZE or HALF SIZE

All working drawings are drawn to scale. The scale chosen must be included on the drawing.

Third-Angle Orthographic Projection

This is the most widely used form of working drawing. Its purpose is to provide plan, front and side views of the object in question.

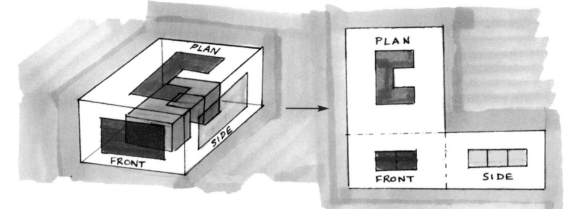

Imagine your product suspended in a glass box ...

... if you draw a view on each side of the box ...

... then open it up as shown above, this becomes your third-angle orthographic projection.

Below is a stage-by-stage set of instructions for how to draw a third-angle orthographic projection.

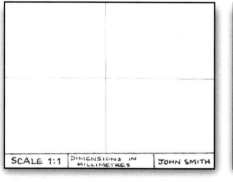

1 Make sure you measure your page first - so all of the views fit on. Then allow a box along the bottom to put scale, dimensions and your name in. Divide your page into 4 using a 2H pencil.

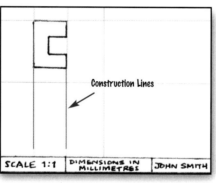

2 Draw the plan view first and leave in the construction lines to help you draw the next view.

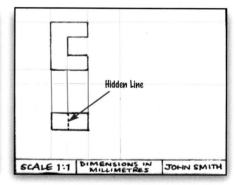

3 Draw the front view with the hidden detail drawn as a dotted line.

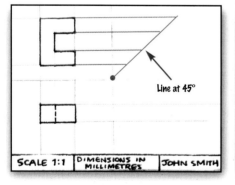

4 Draw construction lines into the top right box. Also draw a 45° line from the centre of the page. Stop the construction lines where they hit the 45° line.

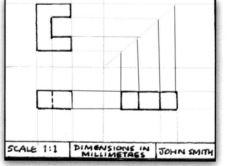

5 Draw lines down from these construction lines to join the horizontal construction lines from the front view, so forming the side view.

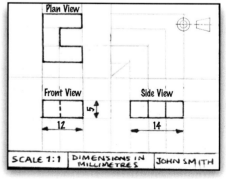

6 Final drawing. Label views. Include major dimensions.

COMPUTER-AIDED MANUFACTURE

The ideal coursework project would use COMPUTER-AIDED MANUFACTURING (CAM) to produce components in quantity. There are many schools which do not have enough of these facilities to make this a reality but you should be aware of what is possible as it might feature in the written paper.

Computer-Aided Manufacture

CAM relies on data known as MACHINE CODE. It is numerical data which explains why the machinery used for CAM is often called CNC (Computer Numerical Control). Drawings are created using COMPUTER-AIDED DESIGN (CAD) packages, therefore the term CAD/CAM is often used as a single process. Nowadays, the machine code is created by the software rather than inputted by a keyboard. This is known as POST PROCESSING.

Two-axis Machines

This means that there are two stepper motors controlling the movements. One axis controls the sideways movement and the other controls the front-to-back movement. Lathes, engraving machines, plotters and vinyl cutters work in this way. These machines are common in schools.

Three-axis Machines

A third axis, up and down, is added which means that more complex machining can take place. Routers and milling machines fall into this group. These machines are becoming much more common in schools and are used mainly for sheet timber and plastics.

Four-axis Machines

The fourth axis allows the work to be revolved at the same time as it is being machined and is very much like the addition of a lathe onto a milling machine. This means that full 3D can be achieved in one operation. These machines are very rare in schools but are common in industry.

CO₂ Lasers

Lasers are starting to be used in schools. They can cut a wide variety of materials, including fabrics, although school models are not powerful enough for cutting metals. They can also engrave materials such as hard plastics and glass. They have massive benefits over other CAM systems for cutting as they remove only the smallest amount of material and provide outstanding accuracy.

Rapid Prototyping

A way of creating full 3D objects direct from a CAD drawing. It builds up layers of wax to make prototypes. This is used a great deal in industry and is now starting to appear in schools. You can do something similar using layers of paper cut on a vinyl cutter, but it is very time consuming.

Although you may only manufacture one final product from your design, it is important that you are aware of the various possible methods of production and how your product could be produced commercially. You should explain this in your design folder.

'One off' Production

This is when one product is made at a particular time. It could be a prototype or a very intricate object. 'One off' production usually takes a long time which very often results in the product being expensive. A typical product could be a display for an exhibition stand.

Batch Production

A series of products (which are all the same) are made together in either small or large quantities. Once made, another series of products may be produced using the same equipment and workforce. A typical product could be a stool.

Mass Production

This involves the product going through various stages on a production line where the workers at a particular stage are responsible for a certain part of the product. It usually involves the product being produced for days or even weeks and in large numbers. This sort of production results in the product being relatively inexpensive but production could be halted if a problem occurs at any stage of the production line. A typical product could be a car.

Continuous Production

This is where the product is continually produced over a period of hours, days or even years. This sort of production very often results in the product being relatively inexpensive. A typical product could be screws.

'Just In Time' Production

This involves the arrival of component parts at exactly the time they are needed at the factory. 'Just in time' means less storage space is needed, thereby saving on costly warehousing. However, if the supply of components is stopped, the production line stops, which then becomes very costly.

Quality Assurance

QUALITY ASSURANCE (QA) checks the systems which make the products - before, during and after manufacture. This ensures that consistency is achieved and that the products meet the required standards. Factors such as equipment, materials, processes and staff training need to be monitored constantly. The customer is an important part of any QA system and may well be involved in the monitoring at various stages.

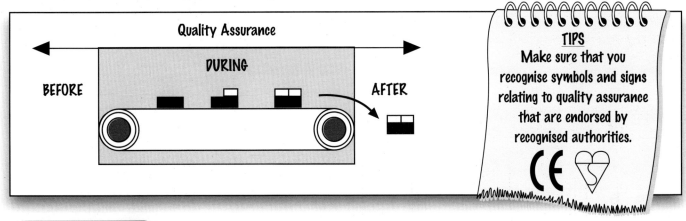

Quality Assurance

BEFORE — DURING — AFTER

TIPS
Make sure that you recognise symbols and signs relating to quality assurance that are endorsed by recognised authorities.

CE

Quality Control

QUALITY CONTROL (QC) is a series of checks which are carried out on a product as it is made. The checks are made to make sure that each product meets a specific standard. Some likely tests carried out on a product include ...

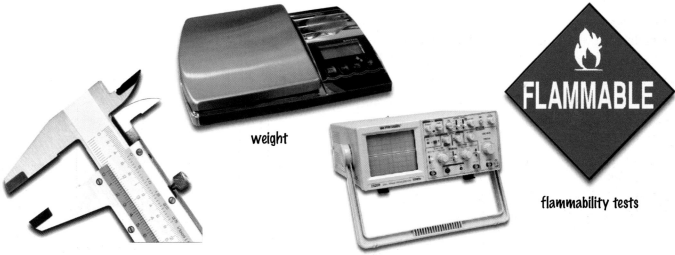

dimensional accuracy

weight

electrical circuit testing

FLAMMABLE

flammability tests

Testing is an important part of the manufacture of a product and can take place at any time during production. For example, an injection-moulded plastic bottle top could be tested after ten, a thousand or a million of them have been produced. In this particular example, some of the tests would include: checking its diameter, its thickness and whether it screws onto its container properly.

Tolerance

As every object cannot be guaranteed to accurately meet the specifications when produced in large quantities, a TOLERANCE has to be applied. This specifies the minimum and maximum measurements. Analysis of tolerance tests can signal the imminent failure of a machine and can help to achieve the ultimate aim of quality control which is ZERO FAULTS. Examples are fixed resistors which have a tolerance of ±5% (gold band) or ±10% (silver band).

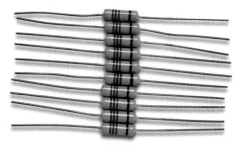

Manufacturing

Commercial manufacturing consists of a system or group of sub-systems which require:

special buildings or places of work.	organisation of people.	organisation of tools and equipment.
quality assurance procedures and quality checks to be made.	information systems to help people communicate with each other reliably.	ways of changing the shape and form of raw materials.
the design and production of many products in a systematic way.	ways of using tools and equipment to transform the materials into products.	efficient and safe working methods.
transportation of materials and finished products.	disposing of waste in an environmentally friendly way.	

This system needs to work together regardless of the scale of production. Feedback from the workforce is essential at every stage if the aim of 'right first time, every time' is to be achieved.

Health And Safety

Health and safety systems are there to protect everyone. In a manufacturing environment these systems have to be checked continually and there are people who manage this. In D & T you will have a number of health and safety systems in place. It is vital that you know what these are as your life could depend on them.

Make sure you know what safety equipment you need to wear.	Always clear away your mess. A tidy area is a safer one.	To reduce the risk of environmental problems and fire, dispose of waste appropriately.
Don't lift heavy items. It may seem cool but it can be very dangerous.	First aid — Do you know what to do if there is an accident? Who do you tell?	Find out what the different fire extinguishers are for and where the fire exits are.

British Standards Institute

Products and components are checked using tests devised by The British Standards Institute (BSI). Each set of tests makes up a standard. BSI standards are very precise specifications and manufacturers who meet these standards are awarded a Kitemark. The Kitemark tells consumers that the product has been tested against nationally recognised standards.

European Standards

This symbol tells customers that the product meets European Standards.

Consumers' Association

This organisation publishes 'Which?' magazine. In each edition, products are tested against other similar products and graded against criteria such as 'value for money'. Many libraries carry Which? reports. Use the same format as Which? reports to conduct your own product analysis. Use the same headings to conduct your own evaluation survey once you have produced a prototype.

Effect On The Environment

As electronic products are becoming more sophisticated and cheaper to purchase, the demand for these products increases. Society's ever-increasing reliance on electronic systems which become out of date very quickly is leading to a throw-away society. Rapid changes in hardware and software design lead to early obsolescence for mobile phones, televisions, radios and domestic appliances. All raw materials come from this planet and, ultimately, all waste produced by obsolete electronic products must return to it in some form. To reduce the impact on the environment you will need to ensure that you:

* use resources carefully
* find another way of solving your problem if your initial solution creates a problem for someone else
* improve your environment - not damage it.

Checklist

Try to answer the following questions with regard to your product:

* Will your product have a detrimental impact on the environment?
* Can you reduce the amount of raw materials used and wasted in the manufacturing of your product and its packaging?
* Can you easily recycle any of the materials used in your product?
* Can you re-use or recycle materials from other products?
* Can you use biodegradable materials?
* Can you reduce the amount of energy used in the production and use of your product?
* Will there be any toxic waste from your product or the manufacturing processes used (such as batteries etc)?
* Are any parts of your product potentially hazardous?
* Can you reduce the amount of energy used to transport your product to the market place?

Recycling

The recycling symbol can be found on many products and the packaging used to protect them. Other symbols and slogans often suggest that the product is environmentally friendly. Do you think that this is just a marketing ploy or is it important for all products to meet this claim?

There is a vast range of construction materials available for you to choose from when designing and making the case to package the electronic circuitry. Materials come in different shapes and sizes and new materials are being developed all the time. It is therefore difficult sometimes to know where to start looking when selecting suitable resistant materials.

One way of starting to select your case material is to look at the PROPERTIES of the material you have in mind to see if it is suitable. You could then look at the COST of the material and its AVAILABILITY. The next thing you could consider is how you intend to make your case - some materials are more difficult to work with than others and can only be worked in a limited number of ways. Finally, you could consider the AESTHETIC qualities or how attractive the material is - some materials are much more attractive than others in colour and surface texture.

To help you, Awarding Bodies list in their Specifications the materials you need to have a working knowledge of, and should be able to cut, shape and form. Check the materials shown in the table below and ask your teacher which ones are part of your course.

MATERIAL	PROPERTIES
PLASTICS Page 47 gives you information about ACRYLIC, POLYSTYRENE and ABS as these are the ones you should know about for your course. But these are not the only plastics you can choose from to make your project.	There are many properties to take into consideration when choosing a plastic for a specific purpose. These are: • Weather resistant • Chemical resistant • Corrosion resistant • Heat resistant • Electrical insulator • Thermal insulator • Wide range of colours • Stiff and hard • Easily injected, blown or formed • Flexible and soft • Impact resistant • Safe to use with food • Self-lubricating • High melting point • Good adhesive • Absorbs shocks • Easily fabricated
TIMBER You should know about PINE, PLYWOOD and MDF. Page 48 gives you information about these types of timber, but you are not restricted to these when choosing the material to make your product.	There are five properties to take into consideration when choosing timber for a specific purpose. These are: • grain pattern - the growth rings visible on the surface • colour - the different tree species vary greatly in colour • texture - different tree species have different surface and cell textures • workability - some varieties are much easier to work with than others • structural strength - different species vary from weak to very strong.
METALS MILD STEEL, ALUMINIUM and COPPER are the metals you should know about, but these are not the only ones you can use for your project. You can find information about these metals on page 49.	There are many properties which need to be considered when choosing metals. These are: • elasticity - the ability to regain its original shape after it has been deformed • ductility - the ability to be stretched without breaking • malleability - the ability to be easily pressed, spread and hammered into shape • hardness - resistance to scratching, cutting and wear • work hardness - ability of the structure of the metal to change as a result of repeated hammering or strain • brittleness - how likely it is to break without bending • toughness - resistance to breaking, bending or deforming • tensile strength - ability to retain strength when stretched • compressive strength - ability to retain strength when under pressure.

Plastics have taken over as the most widely used materials in commercial production. There are two types of plastics with many different varieties and many different properties.

THERMOSETTING PLASTICS can be heated and moulded into shape. If re-heated they cannot soften as the polymer chains are interlinked. Individual monomers are joined together to form a massive polymer.

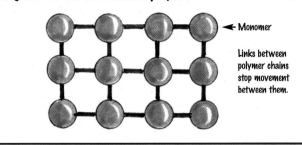

← Monomer

Links between polymer chains stop movement between them.

THERMOPLASTICS soften when they are heated, and can be moulded when hot. The plastic will harden when it is cooled, but it can be reshaped if it is heated up again.

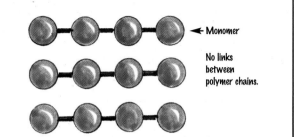

← Monomer

No links between polymer chains.

Acrylic

There are many trade names for acrylic, including Perspex, Plexiglass and Lucite. In its cold state, acrylic is stiff and very brittle and care must be taken to avoid cracking it when it is being cut or drilled. It is a hard-wearing plastic – it is ten times more resistant to impact than glass. Although it will not shatter, it will crack and it scratches easily. Acrylic can be machined and drilled, and threads can be cut into it. It can also be joined by adhesives. When heated, it can be formed, bent and twisted. Acrylic is available in various forms, including sheets, blocks, rods and tubes. It can have a glass-like transparency or be opaque. Acrylic is available in a wide range of colours.

TIPS
When you're working on the acrylic, leave the protective film on to protect the surfaces - you can mark out the required shape on it. Don't forget to remove the film when all the work has been completed. When drilling and shaping acrylic, always wear goggles.

Polystyrene

Polystyrene is much more flexible and less brittle than Acrylic. It is easy to cut and drill and can be spray painted. In industrial applications it can be processed by injection moulding, vacuum forming or blow moulding. It is available in transparent, coloured translucent or coloured opaque sheets. The most common form to be found in a school workshop is the coloured opaque sheet, which can be easily vacuum formed. Polystyrene is used in a wide variety of applications including food containers, toys and the cases for electronic products.

TIPS
The case for your electronic product can be produced by fabricating polystyrene sheets and joining the parts using solvent adhesive.

Acrylonitrile Butadiene Styrene (ABS)

ABS is a thermoplastic material which is relatively stiff, hard and highly resistant to impact. It is quite flexible in sheet form and can be given greater structural strength by injection moulding, vacuum forming and blow moulding. ABS is available in a wide range of colours and various forms, including sheets, blocks, rods and tubes. ABS is often used in applications that make use of its natural resistance to impact, such as for car bumpers, suitcases and the cases for electronic products. ABS is an excellent product-modelling material which can be easily cut, drilled and spray painted.

TIPS
Care has to be taken when machining ABS as its melting point is quite low. Cases for electronic products can be produced by fabricating ABS sheets and joining the parts by solvent adhesive.

HARDWOODS come from deciduous or broad-leafed trees. They are generally slow growing which tends to make them harder. However, not all hardwoods are hard - Balsa, for example, is very light and soft.

SOFTWOODS come from coniferous trees which have needles rather than leaves. Softwoods generally grow faster than hardwoods and are usually softer and therefore easier to work than most hardwoods.

MANUFACTURED BOARDS are timber sheets which are made by gluing together wood layers or wood fibres.

Manufactured boards have been developed mainly for industrial production techniques as they can be made in very large sheets of consistent quality.

Pine

Pine (also referred to as 'deal') is a softwood which is cheap and readily available in a variety of sizes in strips, planks, boards and mouldings. It can be purchased rough sawn, planed both sides or planed all around. It is the most widely used timber for general purpose work. Pine can be cut, machined and planed to a bright, shiny finish. It can be nailed without splitting and can be joined by screws or PVA glue. The colour of pine varies from a pale yellowy cream to a reddish brown. The best quality pine is almost knot free. Pine is normally painted or varnished and can be used for interior or exterior work.

Plywood

A major advantage of plywood is that it is relatively cheap and is available in large sheets and in a wide range of thicknesses. Plywood is constructed from an odd number (3 or more) of thin layers of wood glued together. The greater the number of layers, the stronger the material. The thin pieces of wood are arranged so that their grain directions alternate through 90°. Since wood is much stronger along the grain than across it, this arrangement gives plywood a uniform strength. Plywood is not very likely to warp or split. It is available as standard interior or moisture-resistant exterior grades. Plywood is used in a wide variety of applications - veneered plywood, for example, is used to package electronic products such as audio and television equipment.

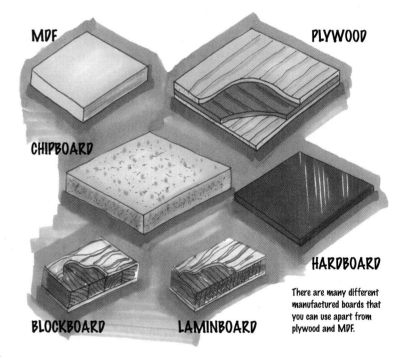

There are many different manufactured boards that you can use apart from plywood and MDF.

Medium Density Fibreboard (MDF)

MDF is a comparatively new material which has become very popular for a wide variety of domestic and furniture uses. MDF is made by bonding wood fibres together with a resin-based adhesive and is available in a variety of thicknesses. The outer surface of MDF is particularly strong, however, the core of the board is much softer. The smooth surface is suitable for a selection of finishes such as stains, varnishes and paints. In the school workshop, MDF is extremely useful for making moulds for vacuum forming due to its closely structured inner core. MDF can also be used for fabricating boxes for projects and can be assembled using PVA glue. For best results, the surface of the project case should be sealed before painting by applying a thin coat of PVA wood glue. If you intend to use a spray paint finish, you should use two or three coats of cellulose sanding sealer as a base layer.

FERROUS METALS are metals that consist mostly of iron and small quantities of other elements and metals. Ferrous metals are prone to rusting if exposed to moisture, and can be picked up by a magnet. Both of these properties are due to the iron content.	**NON-FERROUS METALS** are metals that do not contain any iron. These metals therefore do not rust in the same way when exposed to moisture, and are not attracted to a magnet. Typical examples are copper, aluminium, tin and zinc.	**ALLOYS** are substances that contain two or more metals, and sometimes other elements, to improve their properties. The metals are carefully chosen and mixed to achieve specific properties, such as reducing the melting point. Brass is a typical example.

Mild Steel

Mild steel is the most common type of steel in use and is produced in many different forms. Examples are: sheet, strip, round bar, square bar, rectangular bar, hexagonal bar, and round and square tubing. Mild steel is a good general-purpose steel which can be joined by soldering, brazing, welding and mechanical fixings. Mild steel can be machined by turning, milling, drilling and grinding. It can also be forged, bent and press formed. Although mild steel is softer than most other types of steel, its outer surface can be case hardened. This results in a steel which has a relatively soft core and a hardened outer layer.

Aluminium And Aluminium Alloys

Aluminium is the most common metal on earth and, after steel, is the most widely used metal. In its pure state, aluminium is soft and ductile and is of limited use. Therefore, pure aluminium is alloyed with other elements, including copper, magnesium, chromium, silicon and tin. This results in a selection of aluminium alloys which have a range of hardness and strength. These alloys are used in the production of a wide range of products which includes engine parts such as cylinder heads and pistons, ladders, power cables, drink cans, cooking foil and panels for electrical equipment. Aluminium alloys are used widely in the production of aircraft, and now car manufacturers use aluminium alloys to replace mild steel on body and engine parts.

Copper

Copper is a reddish-brown pure metal which is ductile and fairly strong. Copper is available in a range of shapes and sizes. It can be easily machined, cut, sawn and filed. Copper is an extremely good conductor of electricity and heat and can be soldered or brazed. After steel and aluminium, copper is the third most widely used metal. It is used in many industrial applications including domestic hot water cylinders and pipes, car radiator cores, electric motor windings and electrical cables.

There are many methods used for marking out materials prior to cutting or drilling. Here are some tools that can be used.

Try Square

Used to mark lines at exactly 90° from the edge of the material. Having one accurate straight edge is a requirement for using this tool. Also used as a checking tool when assembling components which need to be square.

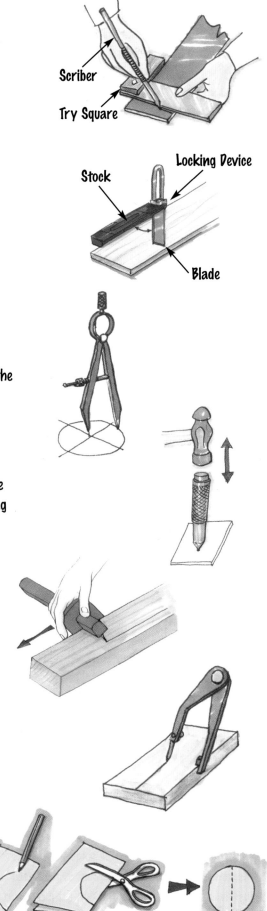

Scriber

Try Square

Scriber

A sharp tool for marking accurate lines on metals and plastics.

Locking Device

Stock

Blade

Bevel

Available as fixed angles (45° for example), or as an adjustable tool for marking any angle. Used in the same way as a try square.

Divider

Used to mark out circles or arcs. One point digs into the material whilst the other point scribes a line into the surface of the material. You should mark the underside of the material if the surface will be seen.

Centre Punch

Used traditionally for marking the centre of holes for drilling into metal. The punch leaves a small indentation which prevents the drill bit from wandering across the surface. You can use this method on soft plastics and timber.

Marking Gauge

A simple tool for scribing lines parallel to a straight edge on timber. It can be drilled to take a pen or pencil so that it can be used to mark a range of materials with lines that can be seen more easily.

Odd-Leg Calliper

These are used to scribe lines parallel to a straight edge and are used for marking metals and plastics.

Card Template

Used for marking out curved shapes onto any material. Symmetrical shapes are best done by folding the template in half and cutting both sides together. Remember to put any templates you make into your design folder.

Being able to hold the material whilst working on it is very important both for efficiency and safety.

WOODWORKER'S VICE - With wooden jaws, this is used to hold timber and plastics to the workbench whilst they are being cut and shaped.

METALWORKER OR ENGINEER'S VICE - A vice which is raised above the workbench and is available with hard steel jaws for heavy metalworking or fibre (soft) jaws for lightweight metal and especially plastics.

G CRAMP - Used for holding material onto bench tops whilst working, and for holding material whilst gluing.

MACHINE VICE - Used for holding material whilst it is being drilled or milled.

HAND VICE - Used to hold smaller and irregular pieces of plastic and sheet metal that will not fit into a machine vice.

SASH CRAMP - Excellent for holding wooden joints together whilst gluing.

SPEED CLAMP - Similar to sash cramps but utilising a self-locking system which makes the positioning easier than a sash cramp.

CORNER CLAMP - Used for holding materials at right angles whilst joining together.

TOGGLE CLAMP - Found as a fixture on vacuum-forming machines but useful when creating jigs for volume production and used for clamping small pieces on a drilling machine.

Jigs are holding devices which are used when manufacturing in quantity. They are often used for accurately drilling holes in components or for cutting material to size. You may need to make a jig or fixture to enable you to save time when making your coursework project or to ensure accuracy. You will gain additional marks for making your own jig or fixture but you must make it available to the moderator.

Jigs

Jigs are specially made for a component or are made adjustable for a range of similar operations. Some jigs are commercially made for a variety of similar jobs.

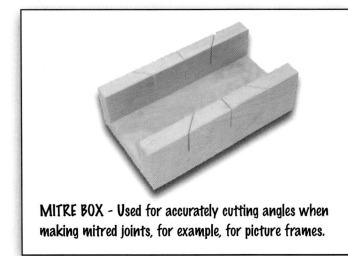

MITRE BOX - Used for accurately cutting angles when making mitred joints, for example, for picture frames.

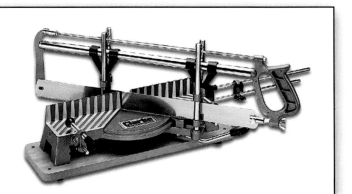

SAWING JIG - An adjustable jig for accurately sawing at a variety of angles.

Fixtures

Similar to jigs but these holding devices are fixed to machines to aid quantity production.

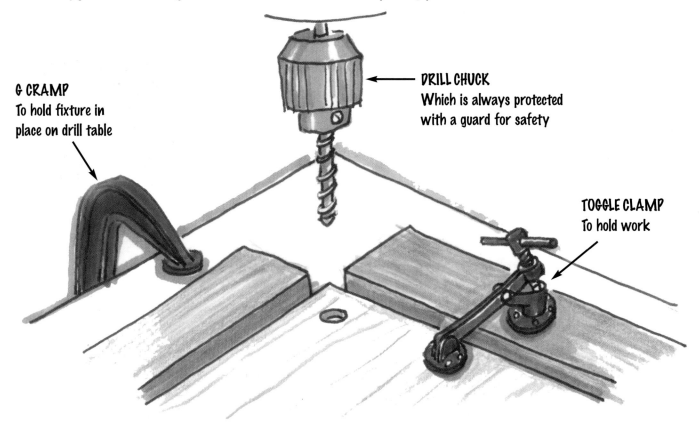

G CRAMP
To hold fixture in place on drill table

DRILL CHUCK
Which is always protected with a guard for safety

TOGGLE CLAMP
To hold work

SIMPLE DRILLING JIG TO AID ACCURATE DRILLING IN EACH CORNER OF THE BOARD

Hand Saws

Sawing is one of the oldest methods of cutting materials. The principle is exactly the same regardless of what is being cut. Teeth are shaped so that they remove a small amount of material on the forward stroke. As a general guide, three teeth should be on the material at any time. There are many different types of saw for different materials and tasks, some of which are powered. Hand-powered saws work on forward or backward strokes depending on the type of saw.

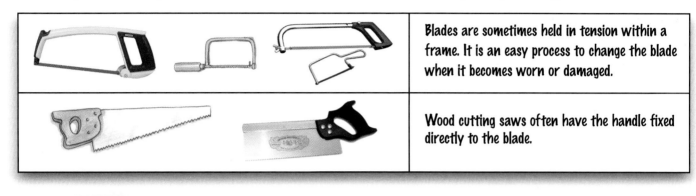

	Blades are sometimes held in tension within a frame. It is an easy process to change the blade when it becomes worn or damaged.
	Wood cutting saws often have the handle fixed directly to the blade.

Power Saws

Powered saws work on several different movements.

Jigsaws move the blade up and down (reciprocating motion). The work is clamped to a bench and the blade is pushed through the material. Although blades are available for plastics and metals, jigsaws are used mainly for cutting sheet timber.

Scroll saws also use a reciprocating motion but the blade is held in tension and moves up and down through a table which can be angled. Blades are available for sheet timber, plastics and metals.

Jigsaw   Scroll Saw

Wood Chisels

There are four types of wood chisel. A sharp edge is essential for them to work properly as they need to slice across the grain.

Firmer Chisel   Bevel-edged Chisel   Mortise Chisel   Gouge

Basic Chiselling Actions

Horizontal paring   Vertical paring   Chopping

Mortising machines can be used to cut deep recesses for joints

Hand Planing

Planing works on a wedge-shaped cutting action and is used to shave off thin layers of timber. Planing can be carried out on some plastics.

Basic Planing Action

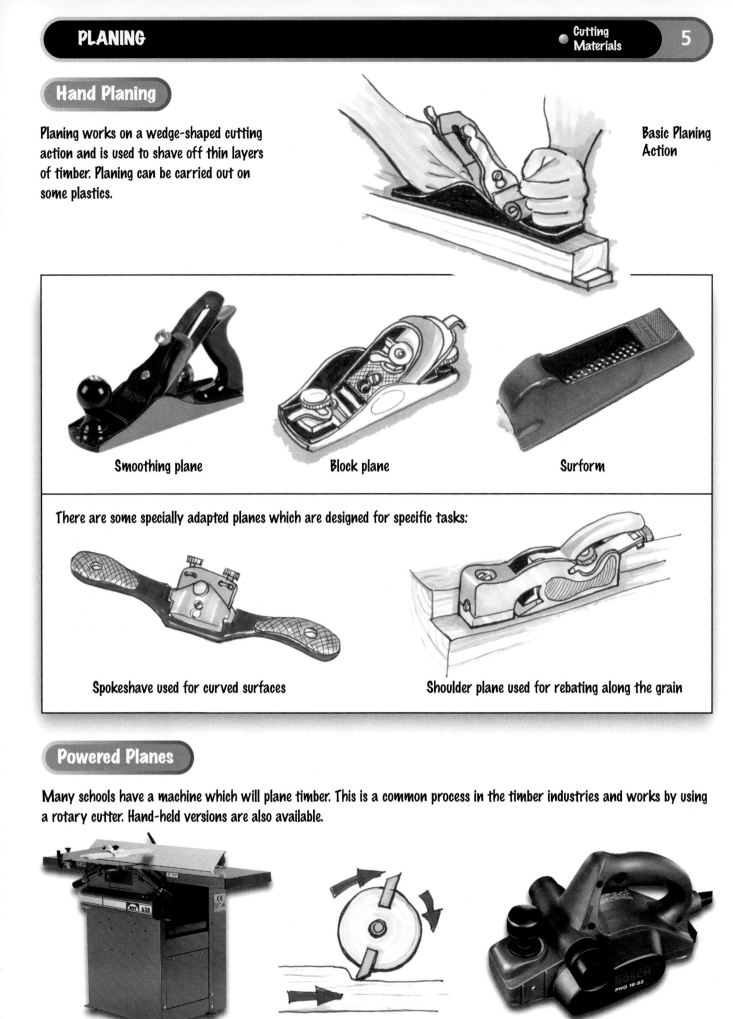

Smoothing plane

Block plane

Surform

There are some specially adapted planes which are designed for specific tasks:

Spokeshave used for curved surfaces

Shoulder plane used for rebating along the grain

Powered Planes

Many schools have a machine which will plane timber. This is a common process in the timber industries and works by using a rotary cutter. Hand-held versions are also available.

Planing machine

Rotary cutting action

Hand-held planer

Drilling By Hand And Machine

Drilling is the process of making holes by rotating a drill or boring bit. All resistant materials can be drilled, it is simply a matter of choosing the correct drill bit for the material. Drill bits are usually made from carbon steel or high speed steel (HSS), although tungsten-tipped bits are used for drilling into brick walls, ceramics and glass.

All drills work on the same principle. The drill bit (or cutter) is rotated in a clockwise direction, either by a hand-powered or electrically powered device, and is pressed onto the material's surface. The drill bits are designed to cut and remove the waste material, although the shapes vary enormously.

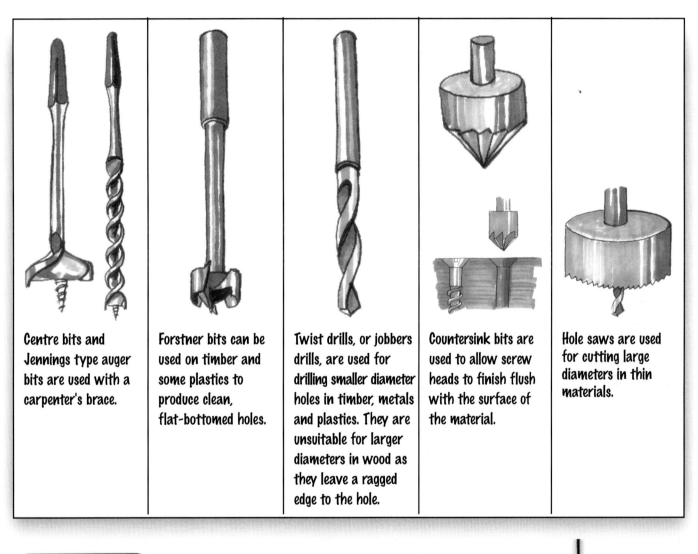

| Centre bits and Jennings type auger bits are used with a carpenter's brace. | Forstner bits can be used on timber and some plastics to produce clean, flat-bottomed holes. | Twist drills, or jobbers drills, are used for drilling smaller diameter holes in timber, metals and plastics. They are unsuitable for larger diameters in wood as they leave a ragged edge to the hole. | Countersink bits are used to allow screw heads to finish flush with the surface of the material. | Hole saws are used for cutting large diameters in thin materials. |

Pedestal Drills

Pedestal drills (also known as pillar drills and drill presses) can be bench or floor mounted. They provide the safest and easiest method of drilling materials that can be lifted onto the drilling table.

PCB Drills

These drills are used for drilling small holes in printed circuit boards (PCBs).

Routing and milling use the same principle of a revolving multi-toothed cutter being moved over the material which is being shaped. When using this technique with metals and plastics it is known as milling. On timber it is called routing. Turning involves rotating the work against a blade. Wood, metals and some plastics can be turned, although the machinery varies. Lathes were amongst the earliest machine tools to be used, dating back centuries.

Routing

Shapes can be cut by manually using a powered router. This can be used to follow a template, used with a guide to cut slots or used to shape the edge of a timber board.

A hand-held router with guide attached for cutting slots parallel to the edge of a board.

The cutter turns into the material.

Milling

Milling machines have clamps to hold the material on to the machine bed. The machine bed can be moved left and right (x axis) and fowards and backwards (y axis) and the cutter can be raised or lowered (z axis).

CNC Milling

Traditional milling machines can be controlled by moving each axis manually. By moving each axis with a stepper motor, very accurate movements can be controlled using Computer Numerical Control (CNC). This is one of the most common forms of Computer-Aided Manufacture (CAM). CNC routers are very common in the furniture industry and work on the same principle.

Turning On A Centre Lathe

Turning metals and plastics on a centre lathe involves holding the work (usually in a chuck) and rotating the work towards the cutter. The cutter can be moved left and right and forwards and backwards. The tailstock can be used to support long pieces of material or it can be fitted with a drill chuck for drilling holes into the end of the material.

CNC Turning

The movements of both the work and the cutting tools can be controlled on centre lathes using stepper motors. This allows the lathe to be numerically controlled. CNC lathes are particularly useful for turning quantities of identical pieces.

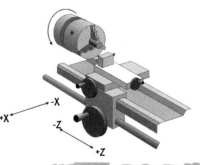

Abrading can be achieved using a wide range of tools which cut away very small particles of material. These include abrasive papers and files.

Abrasive Papers And Cloth

The small chips of abrasive material are glued onto a paper or cloth backing sheet. The abrasive material might be garnet, glass, silicon carbide or emery. Each sheet is numbered. The smaller the number, the coarser the sheet.

Emery cloth is often torn into strips and used in a two-handed manner. It is designed for use on metals although it is sometimes useful for finishing hard plastics.

Silicon carbide paper is generally a much finer abrasive paper and can be used either dry or with water. It is often called 'wet and dry paper' and is used on plastics and for cutting back paint surfaces. The water helps to lubricate the cutting action and remove the waste material.

FINE

COARSE

WET AND DRY

Abrasive paper is usually held around a cork block. Glass and garnet paper is used mainly for timber but is sometimes used for hard plastics.

Files

Files are used to smooth and shape the surface of metals and hard plastics by pressing and dragging the hundreds of small teeth on the file across the material. There is also a type of file especially designed for timber called a rasp which has coarser teeth. Rasps are made from high carbon steel and should be treated with care because they are brittle and can snap if dropped or abused.

Files come in lots of different shapes.

Hand File   Flat   Half Round   Square   Round   Triangular

Sanding Machines

There are many varieties of sanding machines, all are designed to take off the material as quickly and as easily as possible. In general, sanders can only be used for timber and hard plastics. Some machines are designed for metals and are called linishers. All powered sanding machines create lots of dust which needs to be safely extracted. The abrasive material used on sanding machines is often aluminium oxide glued onto a fabric backing.

Fixed sanders can be rotary or belt sanders.

ROTARY OR DISK SANDING

- An abrasive paper disk is fastened to a faceplate on the end of an electric motor.
- Only the downside of the disk can be used.
- The outer edge is spinning faster than the middle so material is not removed evenly.

BELT SANDERS

- Can be mounted horizontally or vertically.
- A revolving belt of abrasive material is powered by an electric motor.
- The belt needs to be supported along its working length by a hard metal surface.
- Material is removed evenly, because all parts of the belt are moving at the same speed.

Hand-held Sanders

A wide variety of powered sanders are now available. Because they are both powerful and portable they present additional safety issues. Always ensure that the material being sanded is firmly held in place and that any dust created is not hazardous to either you or anyone else.

There are many traditional joints which can be used to build structural strength into products - you may need to do further research in this area. The following are a small selection of joints that are commonly used in schools.

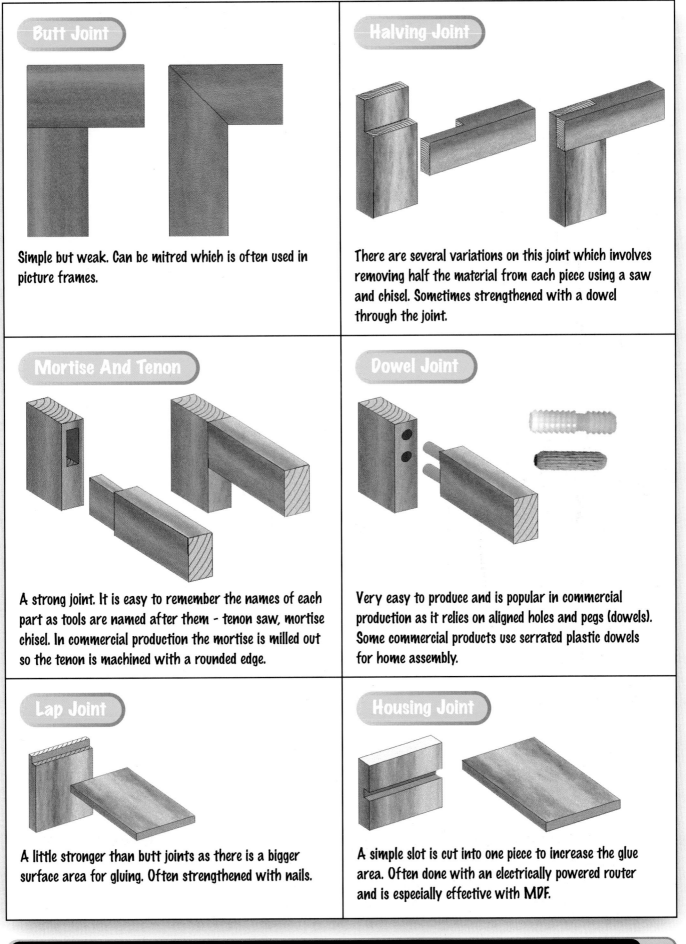

Butt Joint

Simple but weak. Can be mitred which is often used in picture frames.

Halving Joint

There are several variations on this joint which involves removing half the material from each piece using a saw and chisel. Sometimes strengthened with a dowel through the joint.

Mortise And Tenon

A strong joint. It is easy to remember the names of each part as tools are named after them - tenon saw, mortise chisel. In commercial production the mortise is milled out so the tenon is machined with a rounded edge.

Dowel Joint

Very easy to produce and is popular in commercial production as it relies on aligned holes and pegs (dowels). Some commercial products use serrated plastic dowels for home assembly.

Lap Joint

A little stronger than butt joints as there is a bigger surface area for gluing. Often strengthened with nails.

Housing Joint

A simple slot is cut into one piece to increase the glue area. Often done with an electrically powered router and is especially effective with MDF.

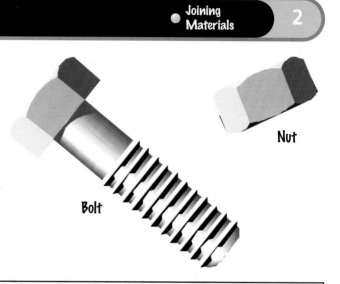

Bolt

Nut

Metals are often permanently joined using thermal methods. Mechanical joining methods have the advantage of being able to join dissimilar metals (and indeed other materials to metals). Some plastics can be thermally bonded although adhesives are more often used. The following methods can be used with both metals and plastics.

Nuts And Bolts

There are numerous variations on this system of joining. Threads are sometimes cut into one piece of the material.

Bolts are made with many different heads. Threads also vary although metric threads are now almost standard in schools - M3 to M12 being the most popular. Available in many lengths, typically 20mm to 100mm. Smaller bolts are called machine screws and have the thread over the entire length.

A washer is usually used under the nut. This might be a plain ring or sprung to keep the nut from vibrating loose.

Washer

Clearance hole

Nuts must obviously match the thread of the bolt and they come in a variety of types and sizes. Wing nuts are tightened by hand and are useful for more temporary joints. Hexagonal heads are tightened with a spanner.

Rivets

Rivets are a more permanent joining method than nuts and bolts. Rivets work by forming a head on both sides of the materials being joined. Pop rivets are a common method.

Pop rivet gun

Rivet inserted from one side

Pin snaps off swelling head on underside

Screw cutting can be carried out on most metals, some plastics and even on some hardwoods, although the latter is a very specialised task usually restricted to the toy-making industry.

Tapping

Internal, or female, threads are usually cut with a tap. This is a very hard steel tool which makes its own thread as it is twisted into the material.

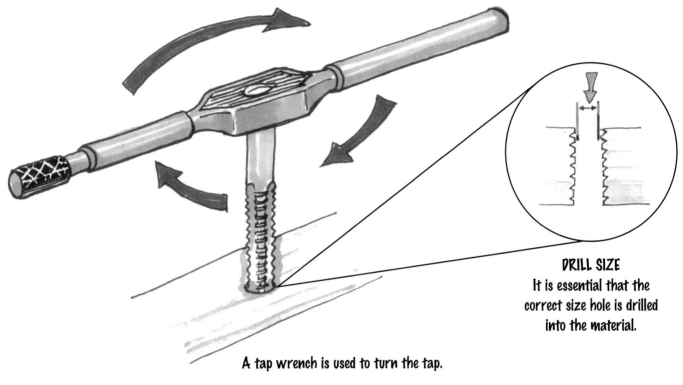

DRILL SIZE
It is essential that the correct size hole is drilled into the material.

A tap wrench is used to turn the tap.

Threading

This is the cutting of an external, or male, thread. The tool used is called a split die and is held in a die stock so that it can be turned.

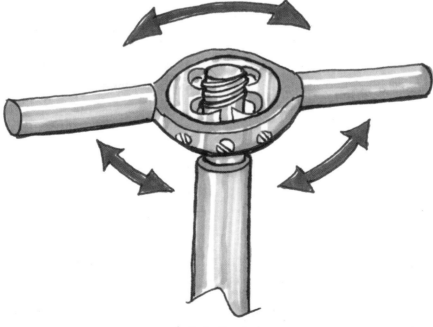

A die in its stock.

Adhesives work on several different principles. There are many specialist adhesives manufactured for specific purposes.

PVA

Polyvinyl Acetate (PVA) is a white, water-based adhesive. The PVA soaks into the surface and sets once the water is absorbed into the wood. It is generally regarded as being stronger than the wood fibres themselves so makes a very strong bond.

Synthetic Resin

This is a waterproof adhesive which needs to be mixed into a creamy consistency with water. Chemical hardening then takes place. It is very hard and brittle. Will set in the plumbing outlet so do not wash the residue down the sink!

Solvent Cement

There are several types available. The most common is Dichloromethane which works by dissolving the surface of hard plastics such as acrylic and high impact polystyrene. Very dangerous fumes are given off so ventilation is essential.

Hot Melt Glue

The use of glue guns is common in schools. Hot melt glue is useful for quick modelling but can rarely be used in final products.

Epoxy Resin

A very versatile but expensive adhesive which will stick most clean, dry materials. Equal amounts of resin and hardener are mixed together and chemically set to form a very hard material.

Contact Adhesive

Both surfaces are coated and allowed to become touch-dry. Adhesion takes place as soon as the two surfaces meet. The solvent fumes are very dangerous and good ventilation is essential.

Latex Adhesive

A rubber solution which is cheap and very safe. Does not give off any dangerous fumes although the smell is not pleasant.

This chart offers some initial guidance but it is always worth testing out samples first, especially when sticking plastics.

	FABRIC	PLASTICS	METALS	WOOD
WOOD	PVA	CONTACT ADHESIVE	CONTACT ADHESIVE	PVA OR SYNTHETIC RESIN
METALS	CONTACT ADHESIVE	CONTACT ADHESIVE	EPOXY RESIN	CONTACT ADHESIVE
PLASTICS	CONTACT ADHESIVE	SOLVENT CEMENT	EPOXY RESIN	CONTACT ADHESIVE
FABRIC	LATEX ADHESIVE	CONTACT ADHESIVE	CONTACT ADHESIVE	PVA

SURFACE FINISHES

1

Many materials need some form of surface finish to enhance them visually and also to protect them from deteriorating. Surface finishes can be applied by a variety of methods including brushing and spraying.

Paints

Paints can be used on metals or timber but are generally unsuitable for plastics. Two types you may use are:
- OIL-BASED PAINTS which usually produce gloss finishes. Durable and suitable for both metal and timber. It is important to prime the material before applying the paint. A good brush or roller is essential. Clean up with turps substitute or white spirit. Most oil-based paints are suitable for use on children's toys and can be used on internal and external surfaces.
- SOLVENT-BASED PAINTS which dry much quicker than other types and are usually available in spray cans. Brush-on varieties are available but are difficult to apply. This type of paint comes in a range of interesting finishes such as hammered, crackle etc. These paints are generally more expensive but can give better results on small products. The correct solvent (often cellulose based) is needed for cleaning up. Good ventilation is essential as these vapours are toxic and a big fire risk!

Varnishes And Lacquers

These are available in oil-, water- and solvent-based forms. Varnishes are clear or translucent and are available in matt, satin or gloss finishes. Spray cans are particularly suitable for small products and there are versions available which have been developed especially for coating metals.

Wood Stains

Wood stains can be used to enhance the colour of the timber and show up the grain patterns. Stains are available in almost every colour but can only be used effectively if they are darker than the natural timber. On their own they are not really a surface finish as they require an additional coating of wax or varnish to protect the timber from moisture penetration. Stains can be water or solvent based or can be supplied as stained varnishes. They are usually applied with a cloth.

Sanding Sealer

Usually a solvent-based product similar to a varnish which is used to seal timber. The quick-drying liquid seals the surface and raises the fibres of the timber so they can be cut back with fine abrasive paper. Suitable as a first coat before applying varnish or wax polish. Works well on top of wood stains.

Plastic Dip-coating

Polythene is the most common thermoplastic powder which is used for this process. Air is blown through the powder to make it behave like a liquid. Metal, pre-heated to 180°C, is dipped in the fluidised powder and returned to the oven where it melts to form a smooth finish. Commercially used for products such as dishwasher racks, it is often used on school projects for coat hooks and tool handles.

Powder Coating

Powder coating is an industrial finish which is a more sophisticated version of dip-coating. The powder is sprayed onto the products which flow through an oven. Modern powder coating provides a paint-like finish and is available in all colours as well as translucent. It is extremely durable.

Self-Finishing

Many products are self-finished. This is true, for instance, of injection-moulded products. The mould is highly polished which ensures that the same surface is transferred on to each product.

63

Injection Moulding

Typical materials used in this process are: POLYTHENE, POLYSTYRENE, POLYPROPYLENE and NYLON.

- Plastic powder or granules are fed from the hopper into a hollow steel barrel.
- The heaters melt the plastic as the screw moves it along towards the mould.
- Once sufficient melted plastic has accumulated, the hydraulic system forces the plastic into the mould.
- Pressure is maintained on the mould until it has cooled enough to be opened.

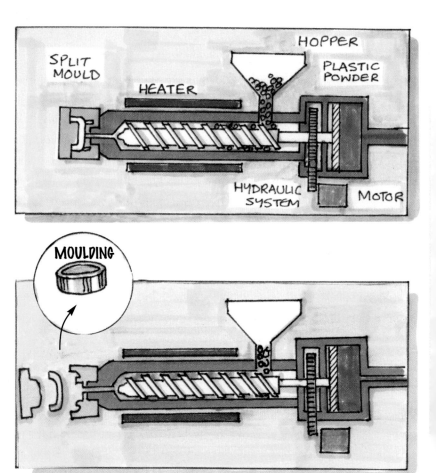

Blow Moulding

Common materials used are PVC, POLYTHENE and POLYPROPYLENE.

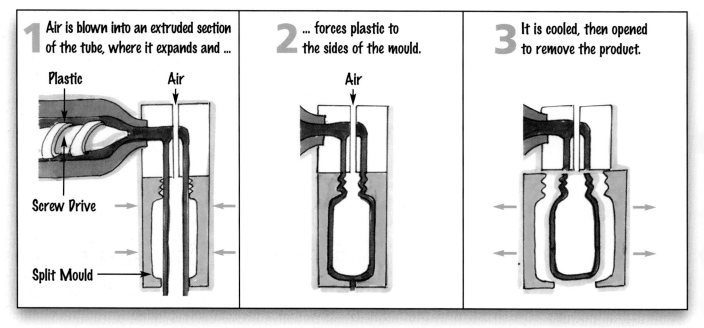

1 Air is blown into an extruded section of the tube, where it expands and ...

Plastic   Air

Screw Drive

Split Mould

2 ... forces plastic to the sides of the mould.

Air

3 It is cooled, then opened to remove the product.

Another method of blow moulding uses an injection-moulded bottle blank called a parison. This is clamped around the screw thread, heated and blown out to fill the mould. This method is commonly used for drinks bottles as it keeps the bottle neck thicker and stronger.

Vacuum Forming

This technique uses thermoplastic materials in the form of sheets which can measure up to 1.5m x 1.8m. The most popular material is High Impact Polystyrene (HIPS) which is cheap and easy to form. The process relies on 'sucking' heated plastic onto the shape of mould that is required.

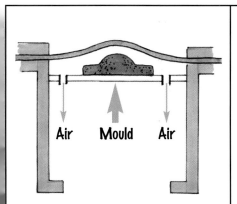

Air Mould Air

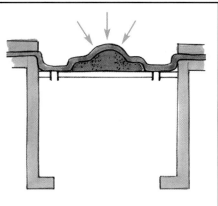

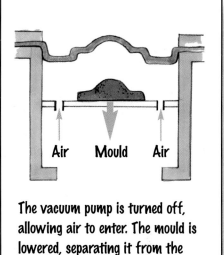

Air Mould Air

The plastic is heated and the mould moves close to it. Air is sucked out to form a vacuum.

Removing the air causes the hot plastic to be sucked onto the mould. As the temperature of the plastic falls, a rigid impression of the mould is formed.

The vacuum pump is turned off, allowing air to enter. The mould is lowered, separating it from the final product.

Line Bending

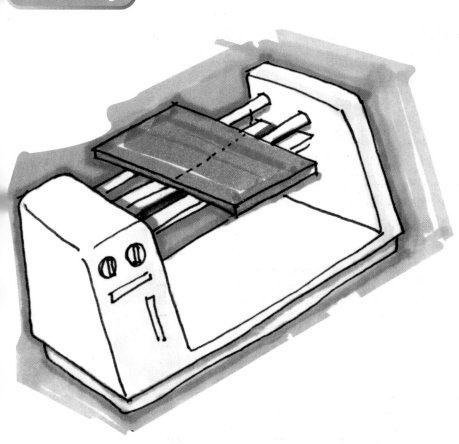

Again, thermoplastic sheets are used in this technique, but this time they are heated only along the line of the intended fold by a special heating element.

Temperature switches control the amount of heat produced to cater for different thicknesses of material.

Acrylic sheets are often used for this process, and bending jigs can be used to produce accurate angles and shapes.

TIPS
Keep your fingers away from the heat element and always remember to switch it off after use.

The choice of power source for your electronic product is an important decision and, like all other design decisions, should be arrived at by investigation. Without a power source, your electronic product will not work! Projects that use mains electricity should be avoided due to the dangers of working with this type of power supply. Batteries are safe, self-contained sources of energy that convert chemical energy into electrical energy. They are available in a range of sizes and voltages which have different internal properties that make them suitable for particular uses.

When selecting your battery, you will need to consider:
- the power requirements of your circuit
- its voltage and type
- the physical size of the battery
- how much you are willing to spend.

The batteries available for you to choose from are:
D, C, AA, AAA and PP3.

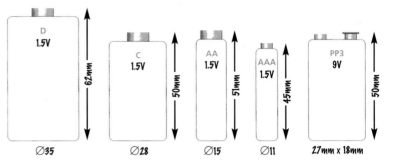

Battery Types

ZINC CARBON BATTERIES are the most basic battery you can buy and are a cheaper version of the Alkaline batteries. They are suitable for projects that do not require high outputs. The voltage level falls during use.	
ALKALINE BATTERIES have a much longer battery life than Zinc Carbon batteries but they are more expensive. The voltage level of Alkaline batteries does not fall as quickly as Zinc Carbon ones. Alkaline batteries have a much higher capacity than Zinc Carbon and provide more amp hours.	
SILVER OXIDE BATTERIES are very small 1.5V button cells which are used in watches, clocks, calculators, cameras and other miniaturised electronic products where the size and performance of power source are important factors. Silver Oxide cells provide an almost constant voltage level until the cell is discharged.	
LITHIUM BATTERIES (NON-RECHARGEABLE) are small 3V disc cells which are expensive to buy but have a very long battery life. The cells are used extensively in miniature electronic products where a consistent and accurate power source is needed. They are used in products such as personal organisers, hand-held games consoles, calculators and watches.	
NICKEL CADMIUM BATTERIES (RECHARGEABLE) are available in all the common battery and cell sizes. Whilst charged, they retain their voltage level well but do not have the same battery capacity or working life as an Alkaline battery. Nickel Cadmium batteries can be cost-effective as they can be re-charged many times. Many electrical appliances, such as cordless drills, use this type of battery.	

Mechanical switches are hand-operated components that are used for making or breaking the flow of electrical current in a circuit. Without a switch, it would not be possible to turn your product on and off. Although there are many different types of switches, they all do exactly the same job - that of bringing contacts together.

SINGLE POLE SINGLE THROW (SPST)

The simplest type of switch is the single pole single throw switch which has one pole and one contact. The SPST switch can be thrown into one contact position only.

Circuit symbol

The SPST switch is also available as a PUSH TO MAKE (PTM) and a PRESS TO BREAK (PTB) switch.

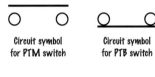

Circuit symbol for PTM switch　　Circuit symbol for PTB switch

SINGLE POLE DOUBLE THROW (SPDT)

The single pole double throw switch has one pole and two contacts and can be thrown into either of two contact positions.

Circuit symbol

DOUBLE POLE DOUBLE THROW (DPDT)

The double pole double throw switch has 2 poles and 4 contacts and is the same as having two SPDT switches in one package. The switch can be used for connecting two circuits at the same time or for reversing the polarity of electronic motors.

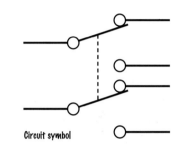

Circuit symbol

The dotted line indicates that the switch arms move together when the switch is operated.

There are many different kinds of mechanical switches - some are shown below.

Slide

Toggle

Rocker

Push

Key

Micro

Reed

Rotary

Tilt

Proximity

Vibration

Resistors are very common components in electronic circuits and are used to limit the amount of current flowing in the circuit and to set the voltage levels in certain parts of the circuit.

Circuit symbol

What it looks like

The Ohm

The unit of measurement for resistance is the OHM (Ω). A single ohm is a very small unit of resistance and therefore resistors are often given the multipliers of R to signify times one, K to signify times a thousand and M to signify times a million. When referring to resistor values in electronics, it is now accepted practice to replace the decimal point with one of the multiplier letters R, K or M. For example, 1200 ohms is 1.2 kilohms which is written 1K2. Other examples are:

5.6 ohms is written 5R6	1 000 ohms is written 1K	1 000 000 ohms is written 1M
47 ohms is written 47R	2 200 ohms is written 2K2	1 500 000 ohms is written 1M5
820 ohms is written 820R	68 000 ohms is written 68K	68 000 000 ohms is written 68M

The Resistor Colour Code

Most fixed resistors are too small for numbers to be printed on them to indicate their value. Therefore, resistors are painted with four bands of colour. These coloured bands are a code which is used to show their value. When reading the value of a resistor, the three bands of colour should be on the left and the single band on the right. The first three bands give the value of the resistor in ohms and are read from left to right. The first two bands state the first two numbers of the resistor's value, and the third band gives the number of zeros to be added. The fourth band indicates the tolerance of the resistor, which is how accurate the resistor is to its resistance value. Resistors can never be made to a precise value, so manufacturers make them to a tolerance. A silver band indicates a tolerance of $\pm10\%$ and a gold band indicates a tolerance of $\pm5\%$.

A 1K resistor with a tolerance of $\pm5\%$

Brown Black Red Gold

A 470R resistor with a tolerance of $\pm10\%$

Yellow Violet Brown Silver

A 68K resistor with a tolerance of $\pm5\%$

Blue Grey Orange Gold

COLOURS	BAND 1	BAND 2	BAND 3	BAND 4 (TOLERANCE)
Black	0	0	x1	
Brown	1	1	x10	
Red	2	2	x100	
Orange	3	3	x1 000	
Yellow	4	4	x10 000	
Green	5	5	x100 000	
Blue	6	6	x1 000 000	
Violet	7	7	x10 000 000	
Grey	8	8		
White	9	9		
Silver				$\pm10\%$
Gold				$\pm5\%$

Preferred Values

Exact values of resistors are not required in most electronic circuits, so only a certain number of preferred values are made to a particular TOLERANCE or accuracy. This ensures maximum coverage is obtained without unnecessary overlapping, using a limited number of series.

E12 SERIES

Resistors with a silver tolerance band ±10% belong to the E12 series which has 12 basic values:

10, 12, 15, 18, 22, 27, 33, 39, 47, 56, 68, 82

Resistors in this series are also available in multiples of 10, 100, 1000 etc. of the 12 basic values. For example, 120R, 1K8, 39K, 5M6, 82M, and so on.

E24 SERIES

Resistors with a gold tolerance band ±5% belong to the E24 series which has 24 basic values:

10, 11, 12, 13, 15, 16, 18, 20, 22, 24, 27, 30, 33, 36, 39, 43, 47, 51, 56, 62, 68, 75, 82, 91

Again, resistors in this series are available in multiples of 10, 100, 1000 etc. of the 24 basic values. For example: 160R, 22K, 6M8 and so on.

Other Types Of Resistor

The resistance value of POTENTIOMETERS (POTENTIAL DIVIDERS) or VARIABLE RESISTORS is changed by moving the wiper along the resistance track. The maximum resistance value is printed on the body of the resistor.

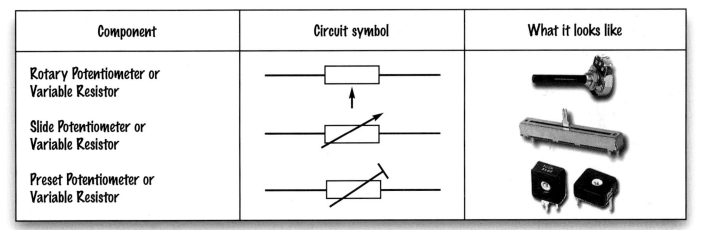

Component	Circuit symbol	What it looks like
Rotary Potentiometer or Variable Resistor		
Slide Potentiometer or Variable Resistor		
Preset Potentiometer or Variable Resistor		

Current Limiting Resistors

Components such as LIGHT EMITTING DIODES (LEDs) and TRANSISTORS can be protected by using a resistor (called a current limiting resistor) which limits the current and prevents the components from being damaged.

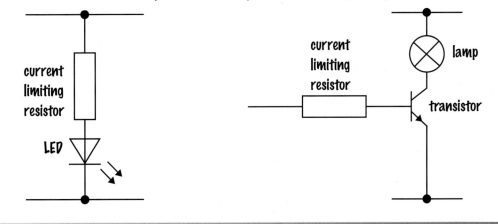

Whilst George Ohm was experimenting with electricity in 1826, he identified a relationship between VOLTAGE, CURRENT and RESISTANCE. He discovered that the current passing through a resistor was proportional to the voltage across the resistor. He found that if the voltage across a resistor was doubled, then the current passing through the resistor was doubled and so on. This became known as Ohm's Law and is probably the most important formula in electronics.

Electrical current flows through some materials more easily than others when a voltage is applied across the material. This opposition to current flow is called resistance and is measured in ohms. Current is measured in AMPS and the voltage across the material is measured in VOLTS.

Ohm's Law states the relationship between current (I), voltage (V) and resistance (R) in an electrical circuit is:

$$V = I \times R$$

Ohm's Law can be placed in a triangle to help you to rearrange the formula. All you have to do is cover up the unknown, and the formula you require can then be read from the triangle.

If you want V then...   If you want I then...   If you want R then...

$V = I \times R$ $I = \dfrac{V}{R}$ $R = \dfrac{V}{I}$

Worked examples

1 What current passes through a 180R resistor if the voltage across it is 9 volts?

Using the formula triangle:

$$I = \frac{V}{R}$$

$$= \frac{9V}{180R}$$

$$= \frac{9}{180}$$

$$= 0.05A \text{ or } 50mA$$

2 A current of 2mA passes through a 1K resistor. What is the voltage across the resistor?

Using the formula triangle: $V = I \times R$

How you work out the answer depends on which method you prefer to use. Here are the alternatives.

$V = I \times R$
$= 2mA \times 1K$
$= (2 \times 10^{-3}) \times (1 \times 10^{3})$
$= 2V$

OR

$V = I \times R$
$= 2mA \times 1K$
$= \dfrac{2 \times 1 \times 1000}{1000}$
$= 2V$

For this method you need to use STANDARD FORM where
$2mA = 2 \times 10^{-3}A$ and
$1K = 1 \times 10^{3}$ (or 1×1000).

For this method you need to realise that a mA is a thousandth ($\frac{1}{1000}$) of an amp. All you do is $\times 1000$ on the other side of the divide line. Also, 1K is equal to 1 x 1000.

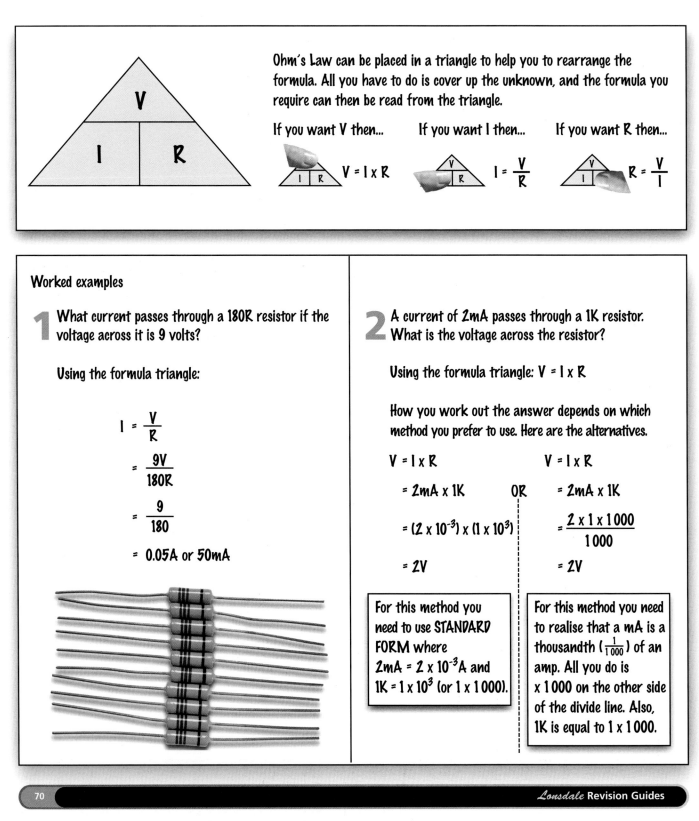

Resistors can be connected together in two ways to give different total values of resistance or to divide voltage or current. This is useful if you do not have the correct value of resistor and you need to make it from other resistor values.

Resistors In Series

When two or more resistors are connected in series, the same amount of electrical current passes through each resistor and the total resistance is equal to the sum of the separate resistances.

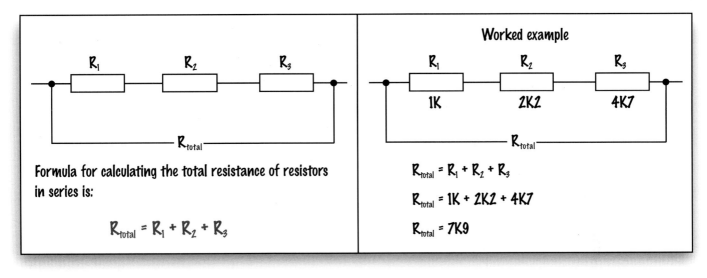

Formula for calculating the total resistance of resistors in series is:

$$R_{total} = R_1 + R_2 + R_3$$

Worked example

$R_{total} = R_1 + R_2 + R_3$

$R_{total} = 1K + 2K2 + 4K7$

$R_{total} = 7K9$

Resistors In Parallel

When two or more resistors are connected in parallel, the voltage across each resistor is the same and the current flowing through each separate resistor is dependent upon the resistance of the resistor. The total resistance is always smaller than the smallest individual resistance.

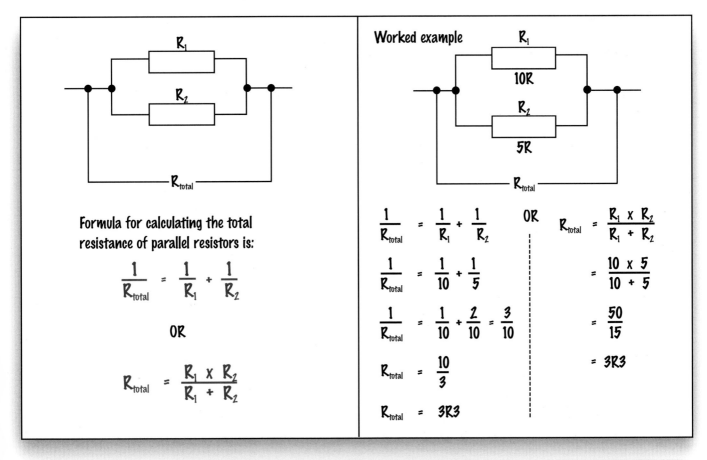

Formula for calculating the total resistance of parallel resistors is:

$$\frac{1}{R_{total}} = \frac{1}{R_1} + \frac{1}{R_2}$$

OR

$$R_{total} = \frac{R_1 \times R_2}{R_1 + R_2}$$

Worked example

$$\frac{1}{R_{total}} = \frac{1}{R_1} + \frac{1}{R_2} \qquad OR \qquad R_{total} = \frac{R_1 \times R_2}{R_1 + R_2}$$

$$\frac{1}{R_{total}} = \frac{1}{10} + \frac{1}{5} \qquad\qquad = \frac{10 \times 5}{10 + 5}$$

$$\frac{1}{R_{total}} = \frac{1}{10} + \frac{2}{10} = \frac{3}{10} \qquad\qquad = \frac{50}{15}$$

$$R_{total} = \frac{10}{3} \qquad\qquad = 3R3$$

$$R_{total} = 3R3$$

How A Potential Divider Works

A POTENTIAL DIVIDER (ie. a voltage divider) consists of the SUPPLY VOLTAGE, V, which is applied across two resistors, R_1 and R_2, arranged in series. The supply voltage, V, is shared across the two resistors with the voltage across the lower resistor being 'tapped off' to become the VOLTAGE SIGNAL, V_s.

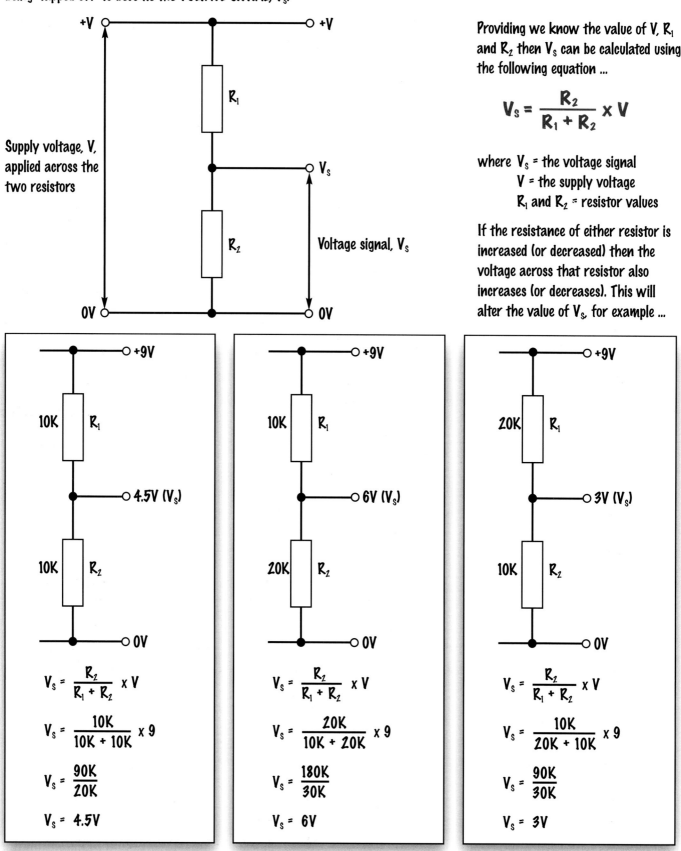

Providing we know the value of V, R_1 and R_2 then V_s can be calculated using the following equation ...

$$V_s = \frac{R_2}{R_1 + R_2} \times V$$

where V_s = the voltage signal
V = the supply voltage
R_1 and R_2 = resistor values

If the resistance of either resistor is increased (or decreased) then the voltage across that resistor also increases (or decreases). This will alter the value of V_s, for example ...

$$V_s = \frac{R_2}{R_1 + R_2} \times V$$

$$V_s = \frac{10K}{10K + 10K} \times 9$$

$$V_s = \frac{90K}{20K}$$

$$V_s = 4.5V$$

$$V_s = \frac{R_2}{R_1 + R_2} \times V$$

$$V_s = \frac{20K}{10K + 20K} \times 9$$

$$V_s = \frac{180K}{30K}$$

$$V_s = 6V$$

$$V_s = \frac{R_2}{R_1 + R_2} \times V$$

$$V_s = \frac{10K}{20K + 10K} \times 9$$

$$V_s = \frac{90K}{30K}$$

$$V_s = 3V$$

NB You will notice that the ratio between R_1 and R_2 determines the value of the voltage signal i.e. the output voltage.

The input to many electronic circuits is from a potential divider. Sensors such as LIGHT DEPENDENT RESISTORS (LDRs) and THERMISTORS are used to give a changing resistance. One of these sensors is often used in conjunction with a fixed or variable resistor in a potential divider.

Light Dependent Resistors

An LDR is a special type of resistor whose resistance changes according to the amount of light shining directly onto it. In darkness its resistance rises to about 10M and in bright light its resistance falls to around 1K. The LDR can therefore convert changes in light levels into changes in electric current.

Circuit symbol   What it looks like

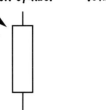

In the following potential divider the voltage signal, Vs, will change from HIGH to LOW and vice versa depending on the light intensity.

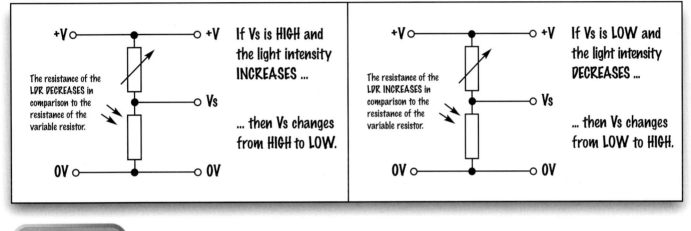

The resistance of the LDR DECREASES in comparison to the resistance of the variable resistor.

If Vs is HIGH and the light intensity INCREASES ...

... then Vs changes from HIGH to LOW.

The resistance of the LDR INCREASES in comparison to the resistance of the variable resistor.

If Vs is LOW and the light intensity DECREASES ...

... then Vs changes from LOW to HIGH.

Thermistor

A thermistor is a type of resistor whose resistance changes according to the temperature. It can be either NEGATIVE or POSITIVE TEMPERATURE COEFFICIENT and respond to temperature in different ways. The resistance of the positive type increases as it gets hotter, whereas the resistance of the negative type decreases as it gets hotter. A thermistor can therefore convert changes in temperature into changes in electric current. The negative type thermistor is the most common and its circuit symbol has a negative sign next to it.

Circuit symbol   What it looks like

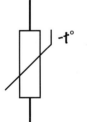

In this potential divider, the voltage signal, Vs, will change from HIGH to LOW and vice versa depending on temperature.

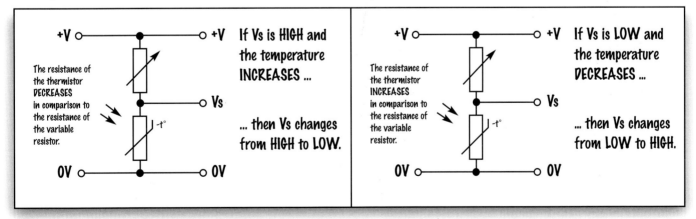

The resistance of the thermistor DECREASES in comparison to the resistance of the variable resistor.

If Vs is HIGH and the temperature INCREASES ...

... then Vs changes from HIGH to LOW.

The resistance of the thermistor INCREASES in comparison to the resistance of the variable resistor.

If Vs is LOW and the temperature DECREASES ...

... then Vs changes from LOW to HIGH.

NB The resistance of the VARIABLE RESISTOR can be adjusted so Vs changes from HIGH to LOW (and vice versa) when the surroundings that the sensor detects are at a particular level. This allows the user to determine the conditions which will switch on the output device.

The most common size of resistor used in electronics has a power rating of 0.25 watts. When current flows through a resistor, it naturally gets warm. If too much current flows, it will get hot and may possibly burn out. When resistors are in use, they convert electrical energy into heat and their temperature rises. The rate of converting energy is called power. Resistors are given power ratings that specify the maximum power at which they can safely work without damaging the resistor. It is sometimes necessary to have to calculate the amount of power being used by a component. This is done by multiplying the current flowing (I, measured in amps) by the voltage across the component (V, measured in volts). This gives the power (P, measured in watts, W).

$$P = V \times I$$

The formula for electrical power can be placed in a triangle and used in the same way as the triangle for Ohm's Law.

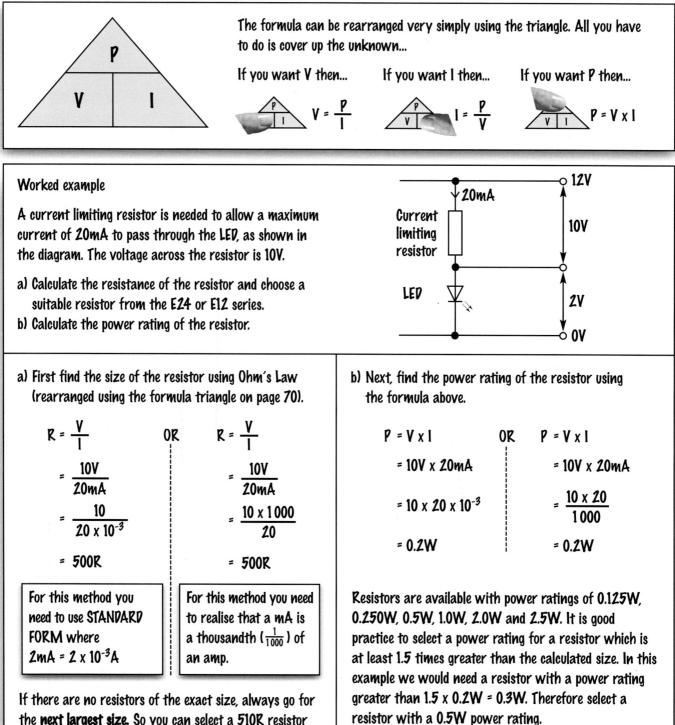

The formula can be rearranged very simply using the triangle. All you have to do is cover up the unknown...

If you want V then... $V = \dfrac{P}{I}$

If you want I then... $I = \dfrac{P}{V}$

If you want P then... $P = V \times I$

Worked example

A current limiting resistor is needed to allow a maximum current of 20mA to pass through the LED, as shown in the diagram. The voltage across the resistor is 10V.

a) Calculate the resistance of the resistor and choose a suitable resistor from the E24 or E12 series.
b) Calculate the power rating of the resistor.

a) First find the size of the resistor using Ohm's Law (rearranged using the formula triangle on page 70).

$$R = \frac{V}{I} \qquad OR \qquad R = \frac{V}{I}$$

$$= \frac{10V}{20mA} \qquad\qquad = \frac{10V}{20mA}$$

$$= \frac{10}{20 \times 10^{-3}} \qquad\qquad = \frac{10 \times 1\,000}{20}$$

$$= 500R \qquad\qquad = 500R$$

For this method you need to use STANDARD FORM where $2mA = 2 \times 10^{-3}A$	For this method you need to realise that a mA is a thousandth ($\frac{1}{1000}$) of an amp.

If there are no resistors of the exact size, always go for the **next largest size**. So you can select a 510R resistor from the E24 series or a 560R resistor from the E12 series (see page 69).

b) Next, find the power rating of the resistor using the formula above.

$$P = V \times I \qquad OR \qquad P = V \times I$$

$$= 10V \times 20mA \qquad\qquad = 10V \times 20mA$$

$$= 10 \times 20 \times 10^{-3} \qquad\qquad = \frac{10 \times 20}{1\,000}$$

$$= 0.2W \qquad\qquad = 0.2W$$

Resistors are available with power ratings of 0.125W, 0.250W, 0.5W, 1.0W, 2.0W and 2.5W. It is good practice to select a power rating for a resistor which is at least 1.5 times greater than the calculated size. In this example we would need a resistor with a power rating greater than 1.5 x 0.2W = 0.3W. Therefore select a resistor with a 0.5W power rating.

NB The larger the power rating the larger the physical size of the resistor.

CAPACITORS are used in electronic circuits to store electrical charge. They are sometimes referred to as short-term batteries due to the similarity between capacitors and batteries when charging and discharging.

Capacitors are frequently used in electronic circuits to:
- create time delays (MONOSTABLE)
- control the frequency of pulse generators (ASTABLE).
- smooth the input across a power supply.

Unit Of Capacitance

The unit of capacitance is the FARAD which is a very large quantity. Because of this, the value of most capacitors used in electronics is measured in microfarads, nanofarads and picofarads. The capacitance value of a capacitor is normally printed on its case.

$$1 \text{ microfarad } (1\mu F) = 10^{-6}F \quad (0.000001F)$$
$$1 \text{ nanofarad } (1nF) = 10^{-9}F \quad (0.000000001F)$$
$$1 \text{ picofarad } (1pF) = 10^{-12}F \quad (0.000000000001F)$$

Working Voltage

Capacitors also display on their cases the maximum working voltage. If this is exceeded, the capacitor will be destroyed.

Types Of Capacitors

Capacitors can be either ELECTROLYTIC or NON-ELECTROLYTIC.

Circuit symbols

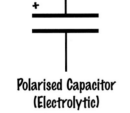

Polarised Capacitor
(Electrolytic)

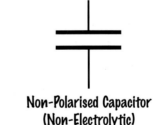

Non-Polarised Capacitor
(Non-Electrolytic)

Electrolytic capacitors normally have much higher values and must be connected in the circuit the correct way around. Electrolytic capacitors are therefore polar components and are available with RADIAL or AXIAL leads. The lead of an electrolytic capacitor which has to be connected to 0V is normally marked with a stripe on its case.

Radial electrolytic capacitor

Axial electrolytic capacitor

Non-Electrolytic Capacitors are normally smaller and have a capacitance value of less than 1μF. They can be connected either way around in a circuit and are therefore non-polar components. They are only available with radial leads.

Capacitors consist of two metal plates separated by an insulating material through which there should be no current flow. This is known as a DIELECTRIC. The metal plates are made from aluminium or tantalum. Various materials are used for the dielectric material including polyester, mica, ceramic and air. As there is no such material as the perfect insulating material, there will always be a small leakage current. The smaller the leakage current, the better the capacitor. Electrolytic capacitors have a large leakage current, whereas non-electrolytic capacitors have a small leakage current.

Charging And Discharging A Capacitor

A capacitor can be charged instantaneously by connecting a power supply across its two leads. However, the rate at which a capacitor charges can be controlled by connecting a current limiting resistor in series with the capacitor.

When a capacitor charges, it takes a certain amount of time to be fully charged and equal the power supply voltage. The rate at which a capacitor charges will depend upon the size of the capacitor and the size of the current limiting resistor. To put it simply:

- the bigger the capacitance of the capacitor, the longer it takes the capacitor to charge.
- the bigger the resistance of the resistor, the longer it takes the capacitor to charge.

The rate at which a capacitor charges through a resistor depends on the product of the capacitance and resistance and is known as the CR time or TIME CONSTANT. This can be calculated using the formula:

Time Constant (seconds) = C (farads) x R (ohms)

To put it simply:

- the smaller the time constant the quicker the capacitor charges (or discharges).

After one time constant, the capacitor would only be charged to about 0.6 of its full charge and would require a further four time constants to be fully charged. The capacitor in the example would take 1 second x *5* = *5* seconds to be fully charged.

Capacitors discharge in the same way that they charge and they would lose about 0.6 of their charge every time constant.

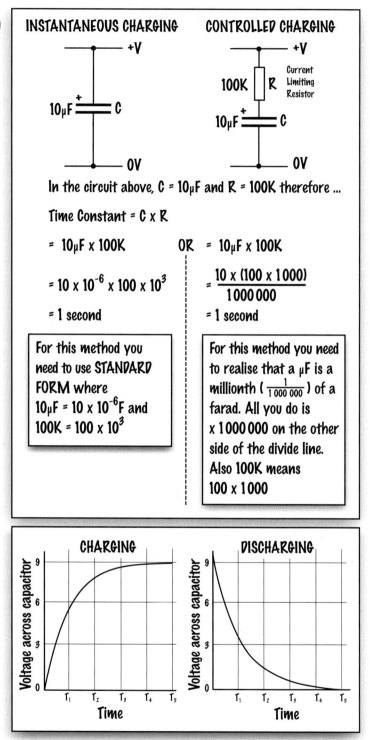

In the circuit above, C = 10μF and R = 100K therefore ...

Time Constant = C x R

= 10μF x 100K   OR   = 10μF x 100K

= 10 x 10⁻⁶ x 100 x 10³

$$= 10 \times 10^{-6} \times 100 \times 10^{3}$$

$$= \frac{10 \times (100 \times 1000)}{1\,000\,000}$$

= 1 second   = 1 second

For this method you need to use STANDARD FORM where
$10\mu F = 10 \times 10^{-6} F$ and
$100K = 100 \times 10^{3}$

For this method you need to realise that a μF is a millionth ($\frac{1}{1\,000\,000}$) of a farad. All you do is x 1 000 000 on the other side of the divide line. Also 100K means 100 x 1000

CHARGING

DISCHARGING

Tolerance Of Capacitors

The tolerance of an electrolytic capacitor can be as high as ±50%, but in most cases it is around ±20%. Due to the large tolerance band, electrolytic capacitors are only manufactured in multiples of 1, 2.2 and 4.7. Electrolytic capacitors can be manufactured with higher capacitance values than any other type of capacitor. In comparison, capacitors such as silvered mica and polystyrene are manufactured to a tolerance of ±1% which results in more capacitance values being available.

As electrolytic capacitors are only manufactured in multiples of 1, 2.2 and 4.7, it is sometimes necessary to join capacitors together in series or parallel to create different values.

Capacitors In Series

When capacitors are connected in series, the total capacitance is always smaller than the smallest individual capacitance.

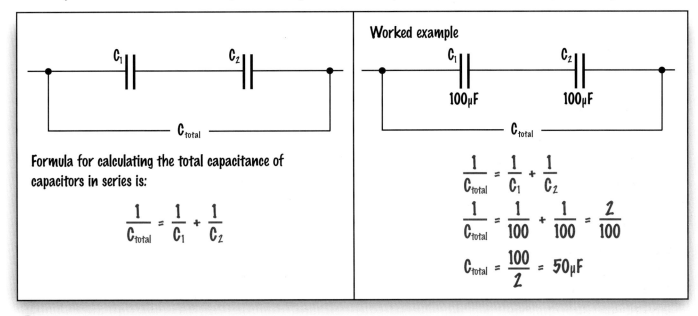

Formula for calculating the total capacitance of capacitors in series is:

$$\frac{1}{C_{total}} = \frac{1}{C_1} + \frac{1}{C_2}$$

Worked example

$$\frac{1}{C_{total}} = \frac{1}{C_1} + \frac{1}{C_2}$$

$$\frac{1}{C_{total}} = \frac{1}{100} + \frac{1}{100} = \frac{2}{100}$$

$$C_{total} = \frac{100}{2} = 50\mu F$$

NB The total capacitance of capacitors in series is smaller than the smallest individual capacitance, whereas the total resistance of resistors in series is equal to the sum of the individual resistances. You will notice that the formula for capacitors in series is the same as the formula for resistors in parallel (see page 71).

Capacitors In Parallel

When capacitors are connected in parallel, the total capacitance is equal to the sum of the individual capacitances.

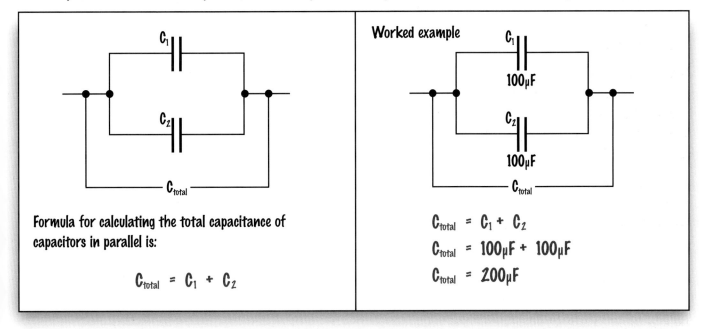

Formula for calculating the total capacitance of capacitors in parallel is:

$$C_{total} = C_1 + C_2$$

Worked example

$$C_{total} = C_1 + C_2$$

$$C_{total} = 100\mu F + 100\mu F$$

$$C_{total} = 200\mu F$$

NB The total capacitance of capacitors in parallel is equal to the sum of the individual capacitances whereas the total resistance of resistors in parallel is smaller than the smallest individual resistance. You will notice that the formula for capacitors in parallel is the same as the formula for resistors in series (see page 71).

A **DIODE** is a component which allows current to flow through it in one direction only. It is like having a one-way street in a circuit.

A diode has two leads: the **ANODE** and the **CATHODE**. A current will only flow through the diode when the **ANODE** is connected to the **POSITIVE** side of the power supply and the **CATHODE** is connected to the **NEGATIVE** side of the power supply. When connected in this way, the diode is said to be **FORWARD BIASED**.

Circuit symbol
Cathode

What it looks like
Cathode

Anode

Anode

How The Diode Works

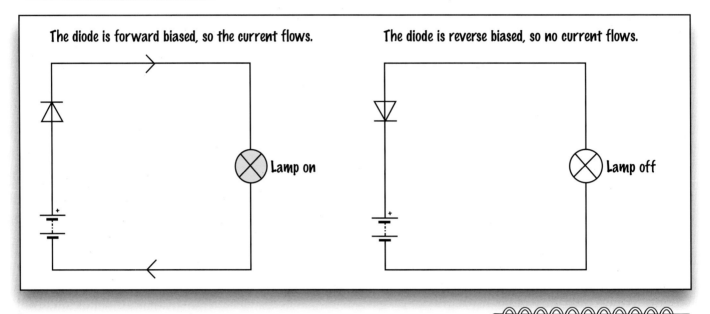

The diode is forward biased, so the current flows.

Lamp on

The diode is reverse biased, so no current flows.

Lamp off

How Diodes Are Used

Diodes are used to:
- protect transistors from back electromotive force (emf)
- protect components against the possibility of incorrect battery polarity
- direct electronic signals to stop feedback from outputs.

TIPS
On a circuit diagram, an easy way to remember if a diode is forward biased is that the arrow showing direction of current is in the same direction as the diode is pointing. The same applies with LEDs.

Protecting A Transistor From Back Electromotive Force

When using a diode in an electronic circuit, it is usual to have the diode forward biased. The exception to this is when you are using a relay (or solenoid) as part of your circuit. When the relay (or solenoid) switches off, a large back emf is created by the magnetic field collapsing around the coil of the relay (or solenoid). Connecting a reverse biased diode across the coil of the relay (or solenoid) will protect the switching transistor from being damaged. Electric motors, when running, can also damage the switching transistor by creating voltage spikes. A reverse biased diode connected in parallel to the motor will protect the transistor. Diodes used in this way are referred to as clamping diodes or flywheel diodes due to the way they dissipate back emf.

Protecting a transistor from back emf

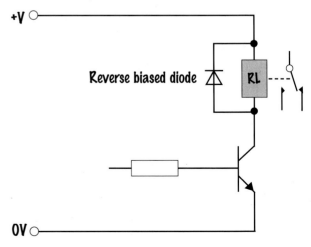

+V

Reverse biased diode   RL

0V

Light Emitting Diodes

LIGHT EMITTING DIODES (LEDs) are a special type of diode which give out light when current passes through them. Like ordinary diodes, LEDs only allow current to flow in one direction. An LED has two leads: the anode and the cathode.

On most LEDs, the cathode lead is shorter and alongside it, on the plastic case, is a small flat. A current will only flow through the LED when the anode is connected to the positive side of the power supply, and the cathode is connected to the negative side of the power supply.

LEDs come in a variety of sizes and colours which include red, green, yellow, amber and orange. Multicoloured LEDs, flashing LEDs and blue LEDs are also available but tend to be expensive.

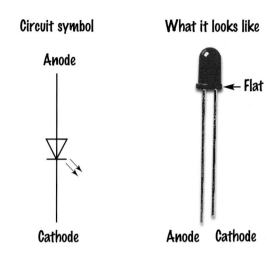

Circuit symbol

Anode

Cathode

What it looks like

← Flat

Anode   Cathode

Using LEDs

When using an LED in your circuit, always limit the current flowing through the LED with a series resistor called a current limiting resistor. A working current of 20mA should not be exceeded. When calculating the resistance that is required, note that an LED needs about 2V across its leads to make it work. This is the formula for calculating the resistance of a current limiting resistor using Ohm's Law (see page 70).

$$\text{Resistance} = \frac{\text{Supply voltage - 2 volts}}{\text{Current through LED}}$$

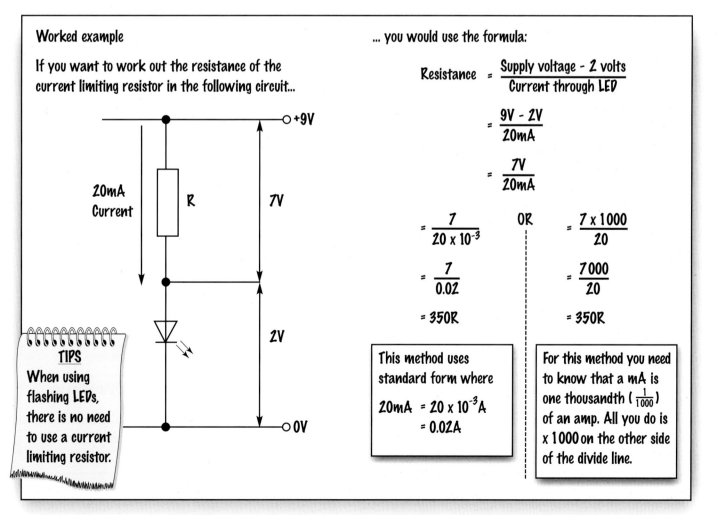

Worked example

If you want to work out the resistance of the current limiting resistor in the following circuit...

20mA Current

R

7V

2V

+9V

0V

... you would use the formula:

$$\text{Resistance} = \frac{\text{Supply voltage - 2 volts}}{\text{Current through LED}}$$

$$= \frac{9V - 2V}{20mA}$$

$$= \frac{7V}{20mA}$$

$$= \frac{7}{20 \times 10^{-3}}$$ OR $$= \frac{7 \times 1000}{20}$$

$$= \frac{7}{0.02}$$ $$= \frac{7000}{20}$$

$$= 350R$$ $$= 350R$$

This method uses standard form where

20mA = 20×10^{-3}A
= 0.02A

For this method you need to know that a mA is one thousandth ($\frac{1}{1000}$) of an amp. All you do is x 1000 on the other side of the divide line.

TIPS
When using flashing LEDs, there is no need to use a current limiting resistor.

Steering Diodes

Diodes can also be used to direct electronic signals to stop outputs from feeding back to other outputs. The circuit below shows a 4017 IC decade counter with its outputs driving six LEDs. The LEDs connect to the 4017 IC to give a rippling effect. The LEDs light in the sequence 1, 2, 3, 4, 5, 6, 5, 4, 3, 2 and so on. LEDs 2, 3, 4 and 5 receive electronic signals from two different outputs and therefore the circuit requires eight steering diodes to stop the signals feeding back into the 4017 IC.

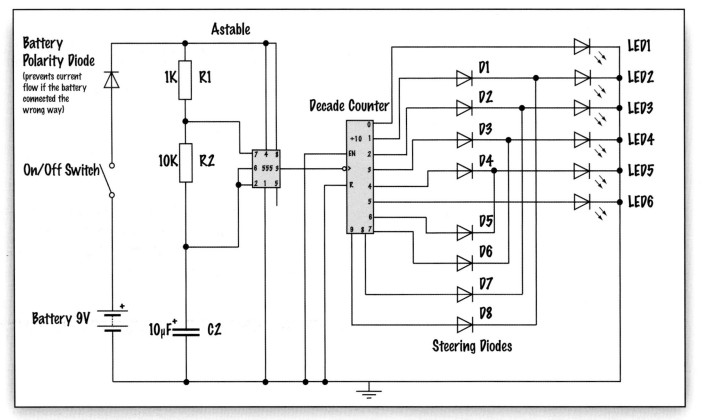

The earth connection connected to the 0V rail is necessary for the circuit simulation to operate correctly. You will note that the decade counter IC has no power connections.

How The Steering Diodes Work

DECADE COUNTER PIN	WHAT HAPPENS
0	Signal sent directly to LED1 which lights up.
1	Signal sent to LED2 which lights up via diode 1 (D1) which is forward biased. D8 is reverse biased so no current goes down this path.
2, 3 and 4	Same as for pin 1, with D2, D3 and D4 being forward biased and D7, D6 and D5 being reverse biased respectively. LED3, LED4 and then LED5 light up in sequence.
5	Signal sent directly to LED6 which lights up.
6	Signal sent to LED5 which lights up via D5 which is forward biased. D4 is reverse biased so no current flows down the path.
7, 8 and 9	Same as for pin 6 with D6, D7 and D8 being forward biased and D3, D2 and D1 being reverse biased respectively. LED4, LED3 and then LED2 light up in sequence.
0	The cycle above then repeats.

The 7-Segment Display

Many pocket calculators, frequency counters, clocks and microwave ovens have something in common – they use 7-segment LED displays to show numbers.

Each display contains 7 separate LEDs arranged in a pattern to form any number from 0 to 9. Each segment location is given a specific letter, from a to g. By forward biasing two or more segments, the numbers 0 to 9 can be displayed. Most 7-segment LED displays have eight internal LEDs. The extra LED is for the decimal point. Depending on the intended application, 7-segment display packages come as either a single digit or as a multidigit LED display, which can contain up to as many as 10 digits.

All 7-segment LED displays are categorised as either common cathode or common anode. A common cathode LED display has the cathodes of all the internal LEDs connected together. In operation, the common cathode is then connected to 0V while the individual segment anodes are each connected to separate current limiting resistors or LED drivers to form the desired number.

A common anode display has the anodes of all the individual LED segments connected together. In operation, the common anode is connected to the positive supply voltage while the individual cathode segments are each connected to ground via either current limiting resistors or suitable LED drivers.

Current limiting resistors must be provided to each LED segment. If a single current limiting resistor is used in the common cathode to ground connection, a variation in LED brightness will occur depending upon the number displayed.

Attaching Flying Leads To LEDs

1 Identify the anode and cathode leads of the LED. The anode lead will be longer. The cathode lead has a small flat on the plastic case. Cut the cathode lead 10mm shorter than the anode lead.

2 Strip the insulation from single core wire. Use RED for the anode and BLACK for the cathode. Insulate the leads of the LED leaving 2mm of the lead protruding from the insulation.

3 Use multi-stranded wire for the flying leads. Strip 10mm of the insulation off one end. Twist the stranded wire and tin. Cut the flying lead leaving only 2mm of the tinned portion remaining.

4 Make a joint between the LED and the flying lead by overlapping the 2mm bare ends. Hold the LED and the flying leads in place with masking tape.

5 Solder together. The soldered joint should be no bigger than 2mm.

6 Slide a piece of PVC sleeving over the soldered joint covering the flying leads attached to the anode and cathode of the LED.

7 Test the LED before soldering into the circuit.

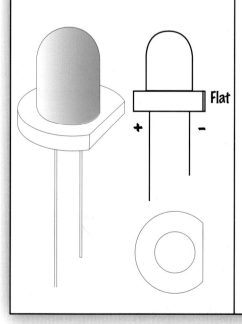
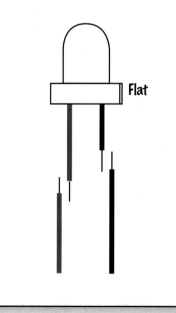

Transistors are electronic switches and amplifiers. There are two types of transistors:

- BIPOLAR TRANSISTORS
- FIELD EFFECT TRANSISTORS

Bipolar Transistors

Transistors are semiconductor devices which are made from three layers of n-type and p-type semiconductor material. Bipolar transistors are further divided into **npn** and **pnp** type transistors. The terms npn and pnp refer to the layers of negative and positive semiconductor material which are used to make the transistors. The sole difference between npn and pnp transistors is the direction of current flow through the transistors. npn transistors are more widely used than pnp transistors.

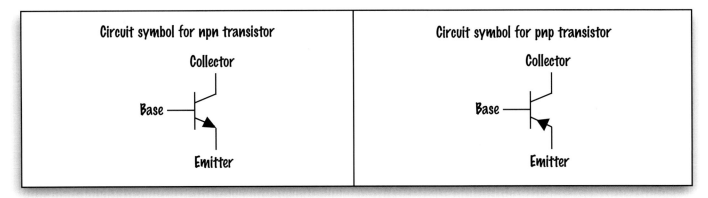

The semiconductor layers form the leads of the bipolar transistor which are called the BASE (b), the COLLECTOR (c) and the EMITTER (e).

A bipolar transistor is controlled by applying a voltage of more than 0.7V to the base of the transistor. This will result in a small current to flow into the base and out of the emitter and will cause the resistance between the collector and emitter to fall. When a transistor is switched off, the resistance between the collector and the emitter is high, and when it is switched on the resistance is low.

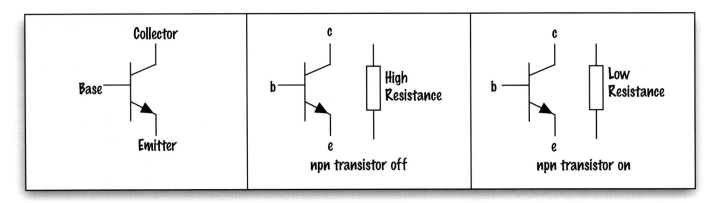

Transistors are analogue devices which allow a larger current to flow from the collector to the emitter as the base current increases. They are used as current amplifiers and electronic switches. A voltage of about 1.5V between the base and the emitter turns the transistor fully on. The switching speed of a bipolar transistor is one millionth of a second.

As bipolar transistors are available in a wide range of case styles, it is important that you identify the base, collector and emitter leads correctly by using a supplier's catalogue, for example, Rapid Electronics.

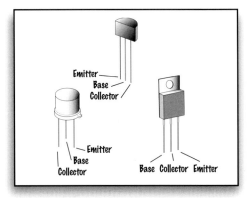

Transistor Calculations

Transistors are current amplifiers and the amplification of a transistor is known as the GAIN. Two current paths flow through a transistor: the base current which is small and the collector current which is large.

With npn type transistors the small current enters the base lead of the transistor and the large current enters the collector lead. Both currents leave the transistor by the emitter lead and become the emitter current. The emitter current (I_e) is therefore the sum of the base current (I_b) and the collector current (I_c).

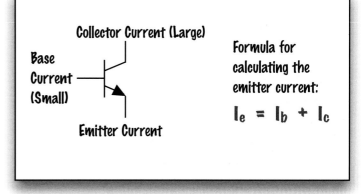

Formula for calculating the emitter current:

$$I_e = I_b + I_c$$

The gain of a transistor is found by dividing the collector current by the base current and is represented by the symbol ^hFE. Formula for calculating the gain:

$$^hFE = \frac{I_c}{I_b}$$

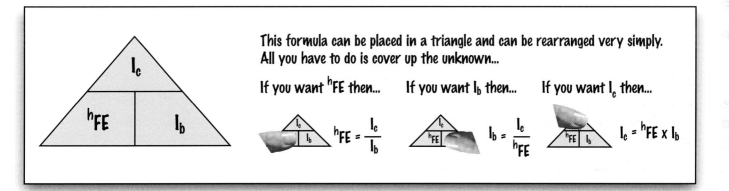

This formula can be placed in a triangle and can be rearranged very simply. All you have to do is cover up the unknown...

If you want ^hFE then...   If you want I_b then...   If you want I_c then...

$$^hFE = \frac{I_c}{I_b}$$ $$I_b = \frac{I_c}{^hFE}$$ $$I_c = {^hFE} \times I_b$$

Worked examples

1 Calculate the gain of a BC548 transistor if the collector current is 100mA when the base current is 0.5mA.

Using the formula:

$$^hFE = \frac{I_c}{I_b}$$

$$= \frac{100mA}{0.5mA}$$

$$= 200$$

2 The ^hFE gain of a BC639 transistor is 40 when the collector current is 150mA. Calculate the base and emitter current.

Using the formula (rearranged using triangle):

$$I_b = \frac{I_c}{^hFE}$$

$$I_b = \frac{150mA}{40} = 3.75mA$$

ALSO $I_e = I_b + I_c$

$$= 3.75mA + 150mA$$

$$= 153.75mA$$

Single Transistor Circuit

The BC548 transistor has a gain of 220 and has a maximum I_c current of 100mA which is well above the 20mA required by the LED. The base current will therefore be the collector current (20mA) divided by the gain (220) which equals 0.09mA.

- The input sensor and the 100K potentiometer form a potential divider.

- When the resistance of the input sensor decreases sufficiently the voltage between the base and emitter increases until it reaches 0.7V and the transistor switches on.

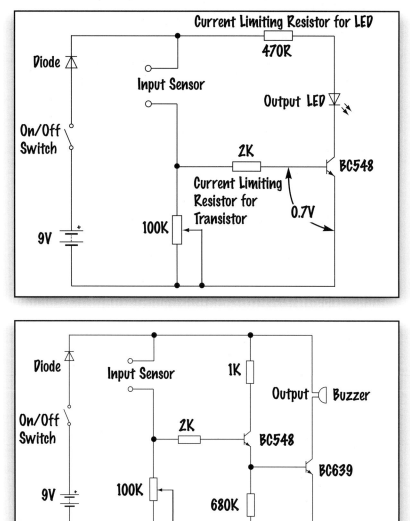

Two Transistor Circuit

By adding a second transistor, the performance of the circuit is improved. The second transistor benefits from the gain of the first transistor and the circuit becomes more sensitive to changes at the input. The second transistor, the BC639 also provides a larger maximum collector current of 1A and can therefore drive electronic devices which require a higher current.

Darlington Pair

A common method of connecting two transistors together is called a DARLINGTON PAIR or DARLINGTON DRIVER. In this arrangement, the emitter current of a BC548 transistor is directly supplied into the base of a BC639 transistor. The total gain of a Darlington Pair is the gain (220) of the BC548 transistor multiplied by the gain (40) of the BC639 transistor.

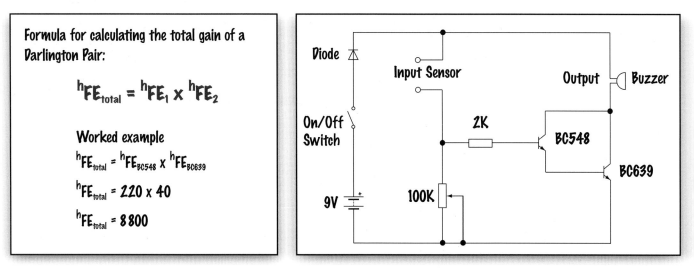

Formula for calculating the total gain of a Darlington Pair:

$$^hFE_{total} = {}^hFE_1 \times {}^hFE_2$$

Worked example

$^hFE_{total} = {}^hFE_{BC548} \times {}^hFE_{BC639}$

$^hFE_{total} = 220 \times 40$

$^hFE_{total} = 8\,800$

Darlington transistors can be purchased in a discrete package which contains two transistors that have the advantage of higher gain and greater power handling capacity. A typical Darlington transistor used in schools is a TIP 120 which has a maximum collector current of 5A and a gain of 1000 when the collector current is 3A.

Like bipolar transistors, FETs are semiconductor devices and are made from a combination of n-type and p-type semiconductor material. FETs, like bipolar transistors, also have three leads. These are called the DRAIN (d), the GATE (g) and the SOURCE (s).

A FET amplifies the voltage at its gate in order to gain an increase in voltage or current. Unlike bipolar transistors, the current flowing between the drain and the source does not depend on the size of the current on the gate.

FETs are voltage controlled and once the gate is triggered by an input voltage of above 2V, the FET turns fully on. A voltage of less than 2V turns the FET fully off. FETs are therefore an example of a digital switching action. This makes them useful as amplifiers for low-powered process units such as CMOS logic gates, Peripheral Interface Controllers (PICs) and as electronic switches controlled by high-resistance inputs such as touch switches. FETs are often used to control high currents or to switch high-current devices, like motors, on and off.

In normal use, the drain is connected to +V via the output device, the source is connected to 0V and the gate is connected to the input.

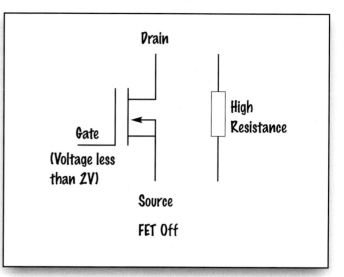

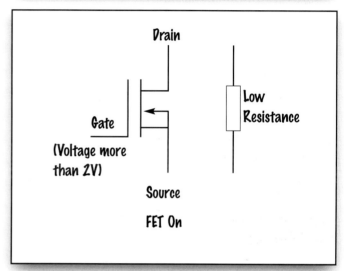

Interfacing

A disadvantage of logic ICs and PICs is that they have a very small power output and therefore require interfacing with other devices to drive higher current loads. The circuit below shows a logic IC or PIC interfaced with a FET and once the gate has been triggered by an input of above 2V this switches on the FET which allows current to flow to drive the motor.

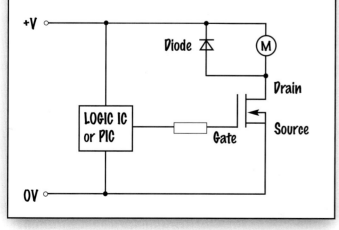

Touch Switch

One of the advantages of a FET is that very little electrical current is drawn into the gate compared to that of the base of a bipolar transistor. FETs are voltage controlled and once the gate has been triggered by an input of above 2V, the FET turns fully on. Bridging the touch contacts with a finger increases the voltage at the gate and turns on the motor via the FET.

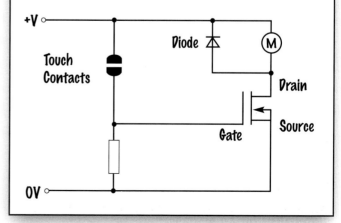

A THYRISTOR is like a diode. It has an anode and a cathode, but it also has a third lead called a GATE.

It is used in electronic circuits to control current flow and to provide a means of keeping a circuit switched on (LATCHING).

A thyristor will only allow current to flow from the anode to the cathode when a voltage of more than 2V is applied to the gate.

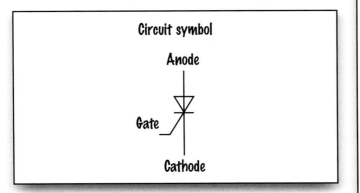

A thyristor is an example of a BISTABLE device. These are devices which have two stable states and can only be changed by setting and resetting.

Once a thyristor has been switched on, it will stay switched on (latched) until it is reset by interrupting the current flow through the thyristor or by switching off the power supply to the circuit. The latching action of a thyristor is very useful in alarm projects.

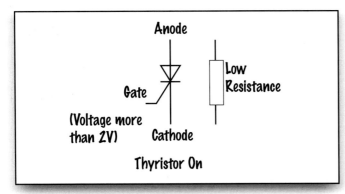

When a thyristor is switched off, there is high resistance between the anode and the cathode leads. The switching voltage of above 2V causes the resistance between the anode and cathode to fall and allows current to flow.

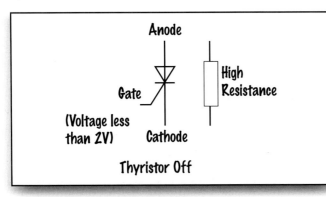

Colour Coding A Thyristor

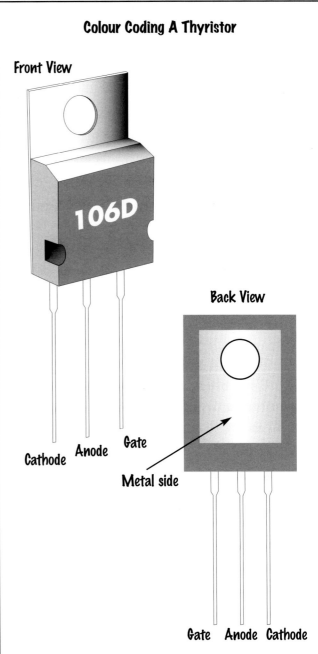

- Identify the cathode, anode and gate of the thyristor.
- Hold the leads of the thyristor between finger and thumb with the metal side facing towards you and the leads pointing downwards.
- The gate is on the left.
- The anode is the centre connection.
- The cathode is on the right.
- Strip the insulation from single core wire.
- Use black for the cathode.
- Use red for the anode.
- Use yellow for the gate.
- Slide about 5mm of each colour onto the relevant pin connection.
- The Rapid Electronics catalogue can be used by pupils to identify the pin connections.

Using Thyristors In Circuits

The thyristor is simple to use and is a relatively cheap way of making an electronic latch. Thyristors are an ideal device to use in alarm circuits and can be triggered by a variety of inputs such as tilt switches, vibration switches, membrane switches, reed switches and piezo transducers.

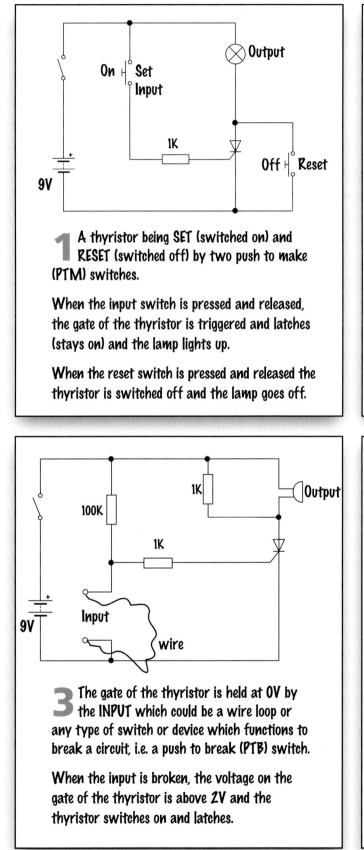

1 A thyristor being SET (switched on) and RESET (switched off) by two push to make (PTM) switches.

When the input switch is pressed and released, the gate of the thyristor is triggered and latches (stays on) and the lamp lights up.

When the reset switch is pressed and released the thyristor is switched off and the lamp goes off.

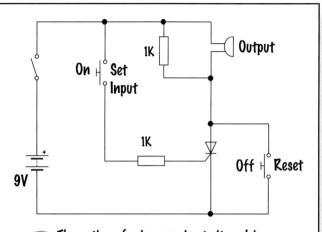

2 The action of a buzzer, due to its pulsing on/off action, can sometimes turn a thyristor off when no current is flowing through the buzzer. To stop this happening, place a 1K resistor in parallel with the buzzer to provide a continuous second current path through the thyristor.

3 The gate of the thyristor is held at 0V by the INPUT which could be a wire loop or any type of switch or device which functions to break a circuit, i.e. a push to break (PTB) switch.

When the input is broken, the voltage on the gate of the thyristor is above 2V and the thyristor switches on and latches.

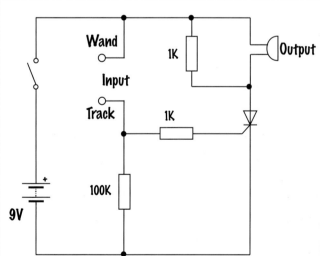

4 The gate of the thyristor is held at 0V by the 100K pull-down resistor due to the input being open circuit. The input could be any type of switch or device which functions to make a circuit. For example, it could be the connections to the wand and track of a steady hand game.

What Is A Piezo Electric Transducer?

A PIEZO ELECTRIC MATERIAL is a material which produces a small voltage when it is deformed through mechanical movement. It also deforms when a voltage is applied to it. A commonly used, inexpensive transducer is made up of a thin slice of piezo electric material bonded to a brass disc.

Circuit symbol

What it looks like

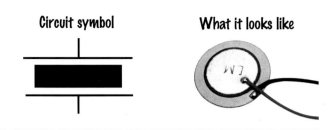

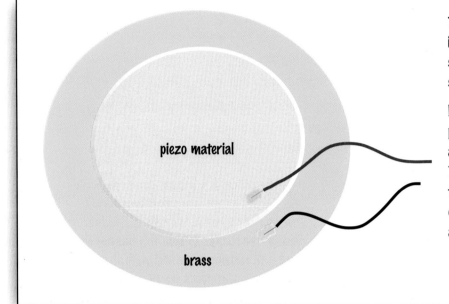

piezo material

brass

The outer disc is brass and the inner disc is the piezo material. Carefully solder red stranded wire to the piezo and black stranded wire to the brass.

If the transducer is tapped lightly, it produces a very small voltage which is able, for example, to trigger a thyristor. The ability to behave in this way makes the transducer a very useful device which can be used as a sensor in many applications.

A Thyristor Being Triggered By A Piezo Electric Transducer

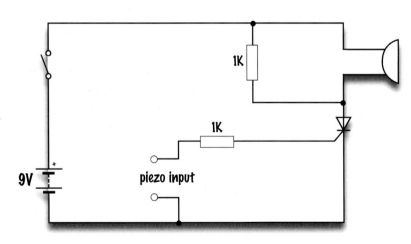

When the piezo electric transducer is deformed through mechanical movement, such as being flicked by a finger, this creates a voltage greater than 2V at the gates of the thyristor. This results in the thyristor latching and the buzzer sounding.

TIPS

Try using a piezo with a 555 IC operating in the monostable mode. Connect the leads of the piezo to pin 2 of the 555 IC and the other lead to the zero volt rail. The piezo works better if the piezo material is made more positive than the brass material. When soldering flying leads to the piezo use stranded wire, colour coded red and black to indicate polarity.

A slight vibration or movement will cause the piezo material to trigger pin 2 of the 555 IC and commence the timing period of the monostable.

Relays

A relay is an electromechanical device which consists of a coil, an armature and contacts. Relays are often used as an interface component between a low-current control circuit and output devices which require much higher currents than the control circuit can provide.

Relays are used extensively in a wide range of products including cars and household appliances, and as well as switching larger currents, a relay can be used to latch a switching circuit. Some disadvantages of relays are that they have slow switching speeds, are relatively expensive and can be quite bulky.

Relays come in many different types and sizes ranging from very large to sub-miniature PCB-mounted relays. Relays are specified by the following:

- type of case, e.g. PCB mounted
- resistance of coil, e.g. 150 ohms
- type of switch, e.g. SPST, DPDT
- switch life, e.g. 1,000,000 switching operations.

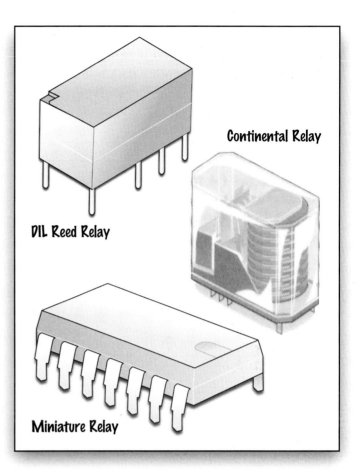

Continental Relay

DIL Reed Relay

Miniature Relay

How A Relay Works

Soft Iron Armature   Pivot   Switch Contacts

Soft Iron Core

Coil

Springy Metal

Coil Connections   Insulation   Connections To External Circuit

Relays use electromagnetism to enable one electrical circuit to switch on a second circuit without an electrical connection between the two circuits. When a relay switches off, the magnetic field around the coil of the relay collapses. This causes a large voltage spike to be created in the relay coil. This is called back emf. Back emf can damage transistors and ICs and needs to be eliminated by using a clamping or flywheel diode (see next page).

The Relay As An Interface Device

The single pole double throw (SPDT) relay is being used to interface a **5V** control circuit to a **24V** output circuit. The relay allows a low-current control circuit to switch outputs on and off in a secondary circuit which can provide greater power. The clamping diode protects the transistor from back emf when the relay switches off.

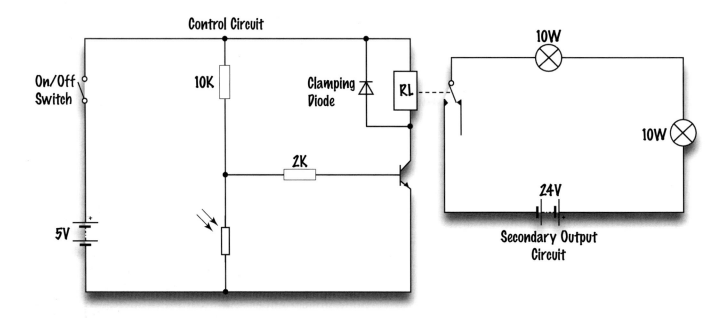

The double pole double throw (DPDT) relay is being used to provide the same interface as the SPST with the addition of a latch. The extra pole and contacts provide an electrical connection across the transistor connecting the collector to the emitter. When the transistor switches off, current will continue to flow through the relay coil and bypass the transistor through the latch as shown on the diagram below.

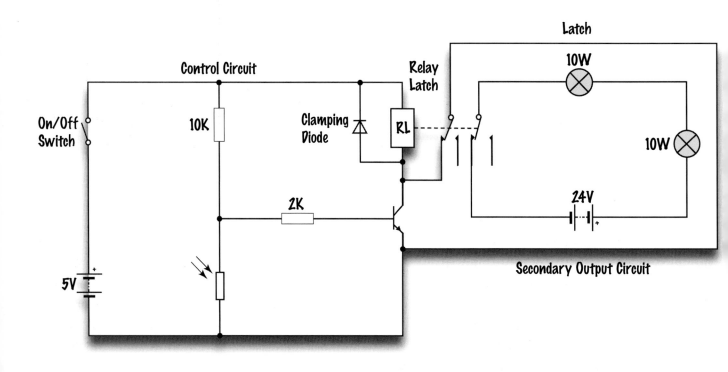

INTEGRATED CIRCUITS (ICs) have revolutionised electronics, computing and communications, and have made possible a vast range of electronic products.

An IC is a complete miniature electronic circuit on a chip packaged in a plastic case. The chip is a wafer-thin piece of silicon no more than 5mm square which can contain thousands of electronic components.

Advanced photographic processes create very small patterns on the silicon wafer to form micro-sized electronic components such as resistors, capacitors, diodes and transistors. Silicon is a semiconductor material. This means that transistors and diodes can also be made and included in the circuit. All connections between the components are made by photography which results in ICs that require little work to make and are therefore relatively cheap to purchase. Connections are made from the silicon chip to metal pins on the package. Most ICs are available in rectangular plastic packages with two rows of metal connecting pins. This type of IC package is known as Dual In Line (DIL) package.

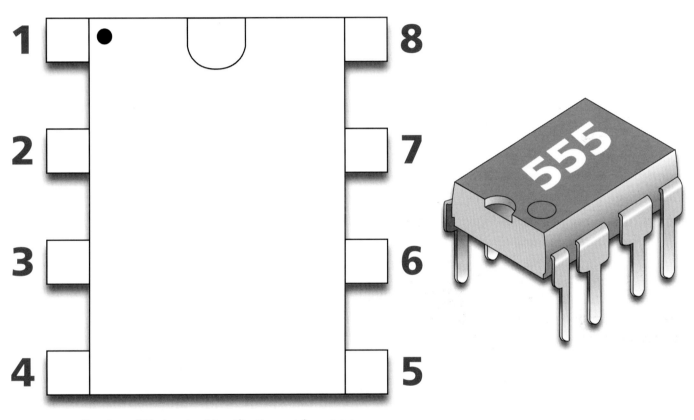

Top view of IC showing identification notch and dot

ICs have a common numbering system for the connecting pins. On the top of the IC at one end is a small notch which identifies pin 1 and the highest numbered pin. With the small notch at the top of the IC, pin 1 is always the top left pin and the highest numbered pin is directly opposite. Some ICs also have a small dot to indicate pin 1. ICs are always numbered in an anti-clockwise direction and can have between 4 and 64 pins.

IC Sockets

When using ICs it is good practice to assemble them on the printed circuit board in an IC socket. By using an IC socket there is little chance of the IC being damaged by the heat from the soldering iron and, if need be, the IC can be quickly removed without needing to be de-soldered. IC sockets have a notch at one end to indicate the position of pin 1 and are available in a range of pin sizes from 6 to 40 pins. When soldering IC sockets onto a PCB, the pins should be pushed through the holes in the copper pads so that the IC socket lies flat on the non-copper side. The pins of the IC socket should never be bent over prior to soldering as this makes it virtually impossible to remove the socket by de-soldering. To keep the IC socket in place whilst it is being soldered, it can be held in position with masking tape.

- **555** Timers are ICs which were introduced in 1972 and are contained in an 8 pin DIL package.
- **555** ICs are used as building blocks in many circuits, especially those that involve timing.
- **555** ICs are used as the main component in monostable and astable circuits.
- A **555** IC can be used in a monostable circuit to switch something on for a certain amount of time and then off - for example, a courtesy light in a car.
- A **555** IC can be used in an astable circuit to switch something on and off continuously - for example, a flashing warning sign on a motorway.

The pin diagram for a **555** IC is shown below.

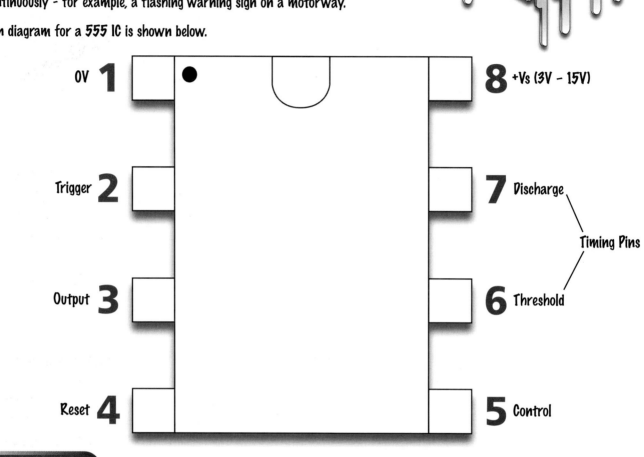

How It Works

- When the voltage at the **TRIGGER INPUT** (pin 2) is less than one third of the battery voltage, the **OUTPUT** (pin 3) goes **HIGH VOLTAGE** and remains high until the voltage at the **THRESHOLD** (pin 6) rises above two thirds of the battery voltage, whereby the **OUTPUT** (pin 3) goes to 0V.
- The high voltage output from pin 3 is approximately equal to the battery voltage minus 2V. The voltage drop of 2V is used within the internal workings of the **555** IC. There are the equivalent of 40 transistors and resistors within the IC package. This is where the 2V is used. Therefore, if a 9V battery is used, the output voltage at pin 3 would be 9V - 2V = 7V.
- When the voltage at pin 3 is 0V, current flows into pin 3. This is called **SINKING CURRENT**.
- When the voltage at pin 3 is high, i.e. battery voltage minus 2V, current flows out of pin 3. This is called **SOURCING CURRENT**.
- The **555** IC is capable of sinking or sourcing a current of 200mA.

Summary

The operation of a **555** IC powered by a 9V battery.

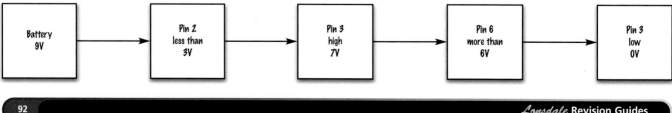

The output from pin 3 is at 0V until pin 2 is triggered by a low voltage. This is the MONOSTABLE STATE of the 555 IC which it always returns to.

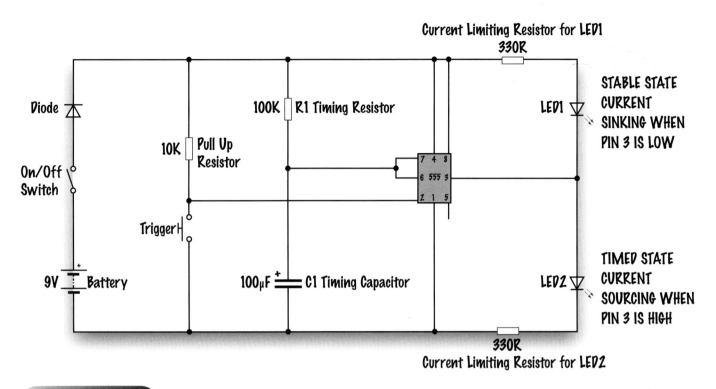

How It Works

- In the circuit above when the IC is in the monostable state, pin 2 is high voltage. Pin 3 is low voltage with current sinking in and LED1 is lit.
- When pin 2 is triggered by being taken to low voltage by a switch or an electronic signal, the output at pin 3 changes from 0V to 7V and stays in the timed state for a set amount of time. Pin 3 is now sourcing current and LED2 is now lit.
- The time period is set by the timing resistor (R1) and the timing capacitor (C1) which are connected to the timing pins 6 and 7 (see next page).
- When the timed period is complete, the output at pin 3 changes from 7V to 0V and stays in this monostable state until the circuit is triggered or switched off.
- The 10K pull up resistor connected to the trigger pin 2 ensures that the voltage on the trigger pin is kept high until triggered by a low input.

Summary

The operation of a 555 IC operating as a monostable powered by a 9V battery.

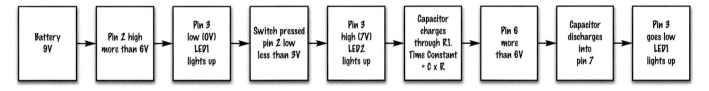

Points to remember when designing monostable circuits:

- The minimum value of R1 should be 1K
- The minimum value of C1 should be 100pF
- The minimum time period is about 0.1µs

- The maximum value of R1 should be 1M
- The maximum value of C1 should be 1000µF
- The maximum time period is about 1000s

Calculating The 555 IC Monostable Time Period

The time that the monostable switches on for after pin 2 is triggered is dependent upon the size of the timing resistor (R1) and the timing capacitor (C1).

The time period can be calculated using the formula $T = 1.1 \times CR$ where 1.1 is a constant. Due to electrolytic capacitors having a large tolerance of $\pm 20\%$, the formula can be shortened to $T = C \times R$.

Worked Example

Calculate the time period of a **555** IC if $C_1 = 100\mu F$ and $R_2 = 100K$. Compare the answers you get using the 2 versions of the formula.

Using the formula $T = 1.1 \times CR$

$T = 1.1 \times CR$ OR $T = 1.1 \times CR$

$T = 1.1 \times 100\mu F \times 100K$ $T = 1.1 \times 100\mu F \times 100K$

$T = 1.1 \times 100 \times 10^{-6} \times 100 \times 10^{-3}$ $T = \dfrac{1.1 \times 100 \times 100 \times 1\,000}{1\,000\,000}$

$T = 11$ seconds $T = 11$ seconds

Using the formula $T = C \times R$

$T = C \times R$ OR $T = C \times R$

$T = 100\mu F \times 100K$ $T = 100\mu F \times 100K$

$T = 100 \times 10^{-6} \times 100 \times 10^{-3}$ $T = \dfrac{100 \times 100 \times 1\,000}{1\,000\,000}$

$T = 10$ seconds $T = 10$ seconds

The difference of 1 second between the two calculations is small when the tolerance of the capacitor is taken into consideration. If a more accurate time delay is required, then a potentiometer or variable resistor can be included in the circuit.

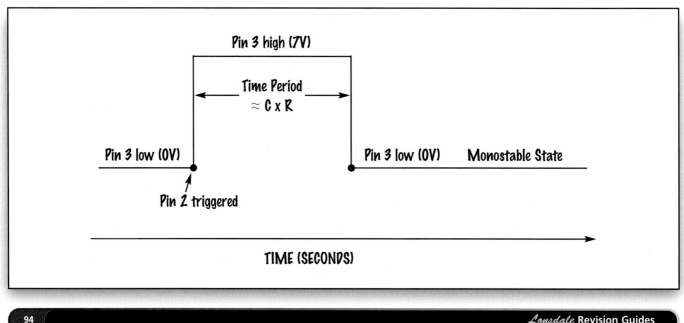

When an astable circuit is first switched on, the timing capacitor, C1, is not charged up, therefore it is discharged and the voltage across the capacitor is less than one-third of the battery voltage, causing the output voltage at pin 3 to be high.

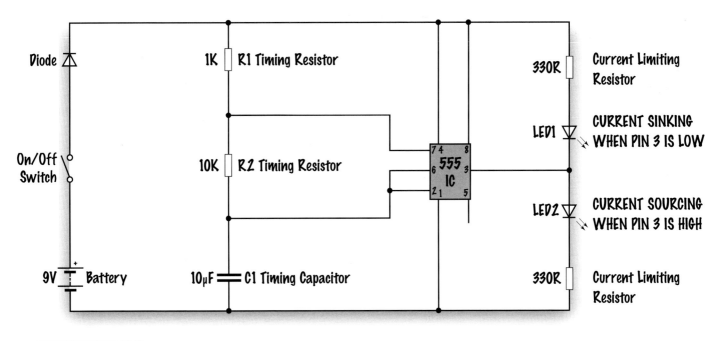

How It Works

The capacitor, C1, charges through the timing resistors R1 and R2 until the voltage across C1 is greater than two-thirds of the battery voltage. At this point, the output voltage at pin 3 changes from high voltage to 0V.

As a consequence, capacitor C1 then discharges through R2 into pin 7 until the voltage across C1 becomes less than one-third of the battery voltage. When this happens, the output at pin 3 changes from 0V to high voltage and continues to repeat the process until the circuit is switched off.

Summary

The process of a **555** IC operating as an astable powered by a 9V battery.

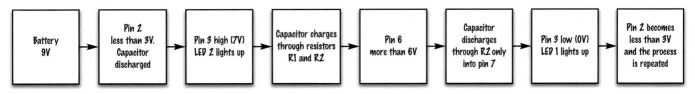

Points to remember when designing astable circuits:

- The timing capacitor C1 charges through the timing resistors R1 and R2, but only discharges through R2. This makes it difficult to have an output at pin 3 which has an equal mark-space (on-off) ratio. If a 1K resistor is used for R1 and a 1M resistor is used for R2, then the error in the ratio of the time the output is high compared to the time the output is low is extremely small.
- When using electrolytic capacitors in timing circuits, it is difficult to produce accurate time periods for monostable and astable circuits. This is because electrolytic capacitors are inaccurate, leak current and their capacitance value changes over time. Non-electrolytic capacitors are more accurate.
- Pin 5, the control pin of a 555 IC, is normally connected to 0V by a 100nF capacitor to prevent the circuit from false triggering. For most school project work, this capacitor is not necessary and pin 5 can be left unconnected.
- Pin 4, the reset pin, can be used to set the output to 0V by being connected momentarily to 0V. Normally pin 4 is connected to +V to prevent any false resetting.

Calculating The Frequency Of The 555 IC Astable

The number of pulses a 555 IC operating in the astable mode makes in one second is called the FREQUENCY. The frequency of the 555 IC is determined by the size of resistor 1 (R_1), resistor 2 (R_2) and the capacitor (C_1). The unit of measurement for frequency is the HERTZ (Hz). The frequency of a 555 IC can be calculated using the formula:

$$f = \frac{1.44}{(R_1 + 2R_2)C} \quad \text{where 1.44 is a constant}$$

Worked Example

Calculate the frequency of an astable if R_1 = 1K, R_2 = 10K and C_1 = 10μF.

Using the formula:

$$f = \frac{1.44}{(R_1 + 2R_2)\,C}$$

$$f = \frac{1.44}{(1K + 2 \times 10K) \times 10\mu F}$$

$$f = \frac{1.44}{(1 \times 10^3 + [2 \times 10 \times 10^3]) \times 10 \times 10^{-6}}$$

$$f = \frac{1.44}{0.21}$$

f = 6.9Hz (Which means there are just under 7 pulses every second)

OR

$$f = \frac{1.44}{(R_1 + 2R_2)\,C}$$

$$f = \frac{1.44}{(1K + 2 \times 10K) \times 10\mu F}$$

$$f = \frac{1.44 \times 1\,000\,000}{(1\,000 + 20\,000) \times 10}$$

$$f = \frac{1\,440\,000}{210\,000}$$

f = 6.9Hz

Mark-Space Ratio

The length of time the output is HIGH (on) is called the MARK and the length of time the output is LOW (off) is called the SPACE.

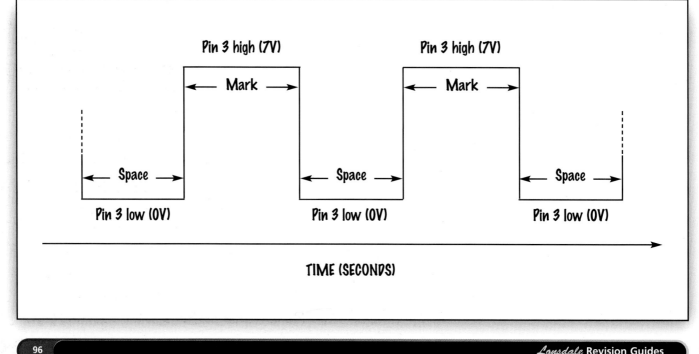

The circuit below shows a **555 IC** monostable circuit controlling a **555 IC** astable circuit. Pin 3 of the monostable circuit is supplying a control voltage to pin 4 of the astable circuit. This voltage is supplied for a time dependant on the time constant of the monostable. During this time, LEDs 1 and 2 will flash at a frequency controlled by the two fixed resistors and the capacitor connected to the astable. When LED1 is on, LED2 is off and vice versa.

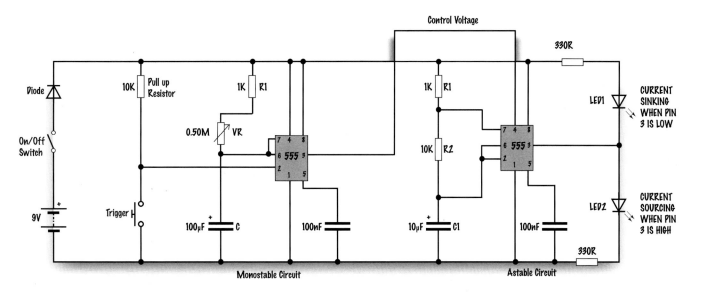

The following mark-space diagram shows what happens in the monostable circuit.

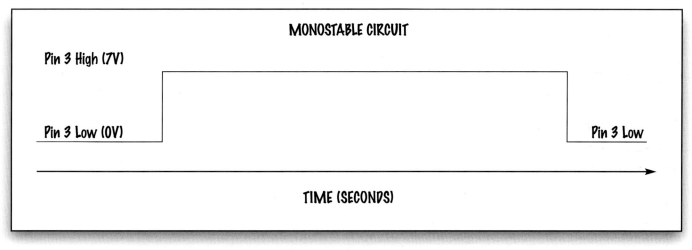

The following mark-space diagram shows what happens in the astable circuit when the output from the monostable circuit is high.

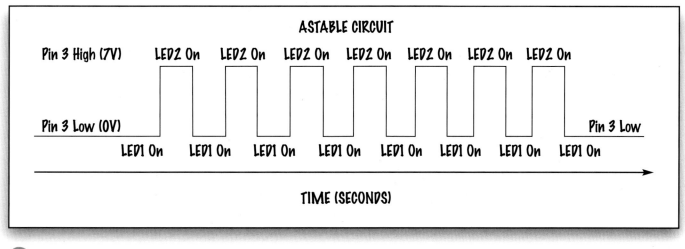

NB The 1K fixed resistor, R, in series with the variable resistor, VR, protects the monostable IC when VR is set at zero resistance.

OPERATIONAL AMPLIFIERS were the first analogue sub-systems to be made as ICs and are often called OP-AMPS for short. Op-amps have two inputs and one output and are usually made as DIL ICs. The 741 op-amp is the oldest type and was, for many years, the most widely used. In recent years, the 3140 FET op-amp, although a little more expensive than the 741 op-amp, has become more popular in schools. Op-amps are available in IC packages which contain one, two or four op-amps in a single IC.

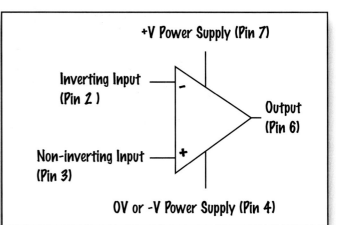

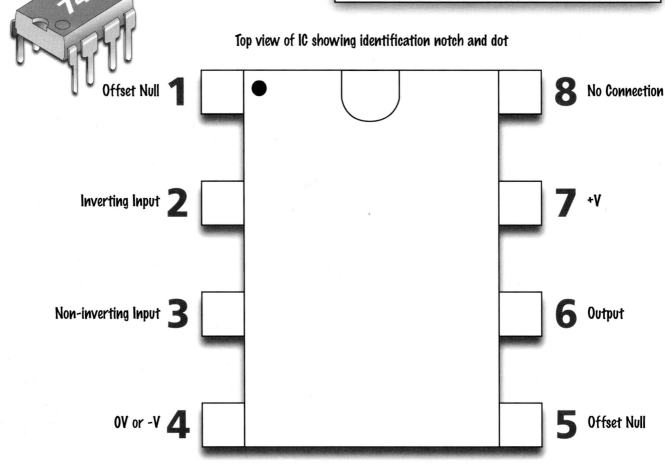

Top view of IC showing identification notch and dot

Offset Null **1**
Inverting Input **2**
Non-inverting Input **3**
0V or -V **4**

8 No Connection
7 +V
6 Output
5 Offset Null

Special Type Of Power Supply

When using op-amps in certain applications, it is necessary to have a special type of power supply which provides a positive (+V), 0V and a negative (-V) voltage supply. Although there are Power Supply Units (PSU) available which provide dual voltages, they are not suited for project work due to size and cost. Therefore, a dual power supply of +9V and -9V can be made by connecting two PP3 batteries together in series. The common connection between the two batteries will be zero volts.

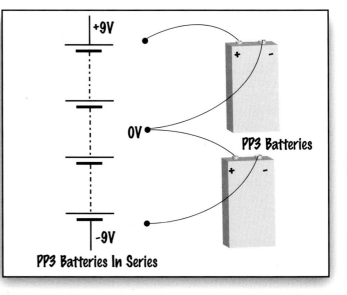

PP3 Batteries In Series

The Op-Amp Working As A Comparator

Op-amps have two inputs: the INVERTING INPUT (marked -) and the NON-INVERTING INPUT (marked +). When working as a comparator, the op-amp compares the inverting input voltage against the non-inverting input voltage and gives a high or low output depending upon which is the greater input voltage. If the non-inverting input voltage is bigger than the inverting input voltage, then the output is high voltage. If the inverting input voltage is bigger than the non-inverting input voltage, then the output is low voltage. The op-amp is able to detect very small changes in voltage between the two inputs and then multiplies the difference by the gain of the op-amp, which is around 100,000 on open loop gain. Any slight difference between the two input voltages causes the output to swing to high voltage or low voltage.

Examples Of Voltage Swing

Pin 2	Pin 3	Pin 6
Inverting Input Voltage	Non-inverting Input Voltage	Output Voltage
5V	6V	High
6V	5V	Low
4.5V	4.2V	Low
4.5V	4.6V	High
4.50V	4.51V	High

An op-amp circuit working as a comparator produces an output which only has two states: high or low. This means that the op-amp is an analogue-to-digital converter and makes it suitable for connecting analogue sensors to logic circuits.

Output Voltage Swing Of An Op-Amp

In practice, 741 op-amps have a voltage output swing which is equal to the power supply minus approximately 2V. The voltage output swing from a 741 op-amp operating with a 9V dual power supply would be +7V and –7V. The voltage output swing from a 741 op-amp operating with a 9V single power supply would be +7V and +2V. 741 op-amps powered by a single power supply will only go as low as 2V output which can cause problems when trying to use op-amps to switch off transistors and ICs because these components need a voltage lower than this.

This problem can be overcome by using the 3140 FET op-amp which operates on a 9V single power supply and outputs to its maximum voltage of 9V and its minimum voltage of 0V. The 3140 FET op-amp is a direct replacement for the 741 and can therefore be used in circuits designed for the 741 op-amp.

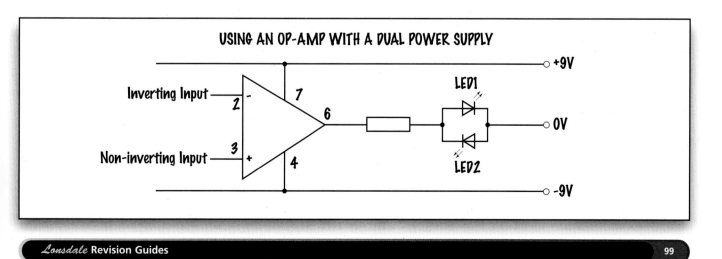

USING AN OP-AMP WITH A DUAL POWER SUPPLY

The circuit below shows an op-amp being used as a light/dark activated comparator. The circuit is powered by a dual power supply of ±9V.

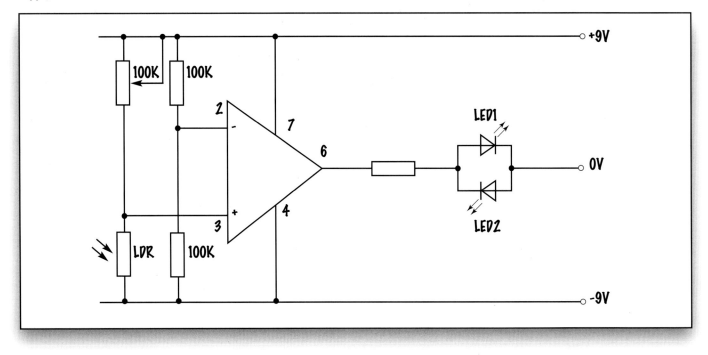

How It Works

- Pin 2, the inverting input is held at a fixed reference voltage by a potential divider made from two 100K fixed resistors.
- Pin 3, the non-inverting input is also connected to a potential divider made from a 100K potentiometer or variable resistor and an LDR.
- The potential divider connected to pin 3 changes according to the level of light falling on the LDR. In darkness, the resistance of the LDR increases and results in the voltage at pin 3 becoming larger. In bright light, the resistance of the LDR decreases and the voltage on pin 3 becomes less and less.
- The 100K potentiometer connected to pin 3 sets the light level at which the comparator switches from LED1 to LED2.
- In bright light, the voltage on pin 2, the inverting input, will be larger than on pin 3 and the output voltage at pin 6 will be −7V. This allows current to flow and sink into pin 6 from the 0V power rail and results in LED2 being lit.
- In darkness, the voltage on pin 3, the non-inverting input, will be larger than the fixed reference voltage on pin 2 and the output voltage at pin 6 will be +7V. This allows current to source out of pin 6 and flow through LED1 to the 0V rail and results in LED1 being lit.

Summary

In darkness...

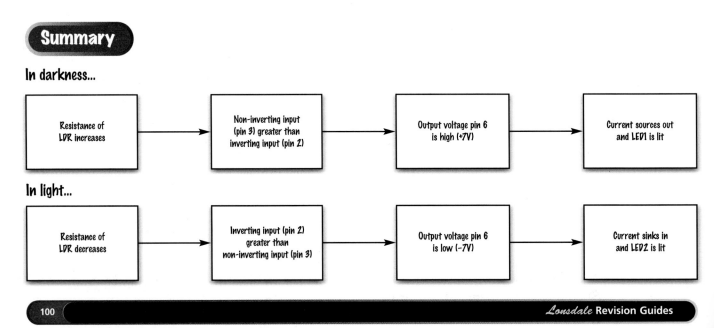

In light...

Using The Op-Amp As An Inverting Amplifier

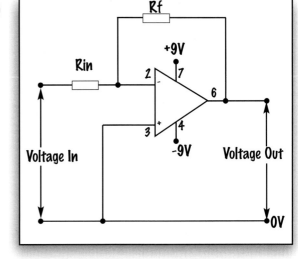

With OPEN LOOP, the gain of the op-amp is around 100,000 and causes the output of the op-amp to swing from high voltage to low voltage, thus giving a digital output. This type of output action can, in some op-amp applications, cause distortion by clipping the output signal. Clipping occurs when the input signal is amplified beyond the size of the power supply. It has to be remembered that the op-amp has a gain of 100,000 and a difference between the inputs, pin 2 and pin 3, of 0.001V would result in an output of 100V which is well beyond the supply voltage of say, 9V. It is therefore necessary, on these occasions, to set the gain of the op-amp to a desired level using NEGATIVE FEEDBACK.

When an op-amp is used as an INVERTING AMPLIFIER, negative feedback is used to reduce the overall voltage gain of the circuit. In the inverting amplifier, the input voltage is applied via the input resistor Rin to the inverting input terminal. The non-inverting input is connected to 0V. Negative feedback is provided by the feedback resistor Rf.

Setting The Voltage Gain

The gain of an op-amp is set by using a feedback resistor (R_f) and an input resistor (R_{in}). The feedback resistor, by feeding back a small part of the output to the inverting input, ensures that the feedback is negative. The advantage of negative feedback is that the op-amp is more stable and the gain predictable. The formula for calculating the gain of an inverting op-amp is:

$$\text{Gain} = \frac{-R_f}{R_{in}}$$

Where R_f = feedback resistor value and R_{in} = input resistor value

The minus sign in the formula indicates that the output will always be inverted in relation to the input. This means that if the input is positive, then the output will be negative and vice versa.

Worked Example

When R_f = 100K and R_{in} = 10K

$$\text{Gain} = \frac{-R_f}{R_{in}}$$

$$= \frac{-100K}{10K}$$

$$= -10$$

(Note that the gain has no units – simply a mathematical value.)

VOLTAGE INPUT   0.1V   0V

VOLTAGE OUTPUT   0V   -1V

For example, if the input is a square wave of maximum voltage +0.1V, then the output will be a square wave of the same frequency of maximum voltage -10 x 0.1V = -1V

The two circuits below show an op-amp operating as a voltage comparator using a 9V single power supply.

The op-amp is triggering the 555 IC monostable circuit by taking pin 2 to low voltage, i.e. less than one-third of the battery voltage.

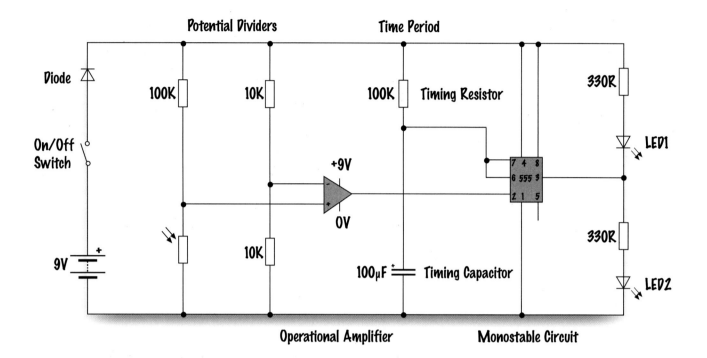

The op-amp is controlling the 555 IC astable circuit by providing a voltage to pin 4 of the astable. When pin 6 of the op-amp is high, the LEDs will be flashing. When pin 6 of the op-amp is low, pin 4 on the 555 IC will reset the output back to 0V and LED1 will stay lit.

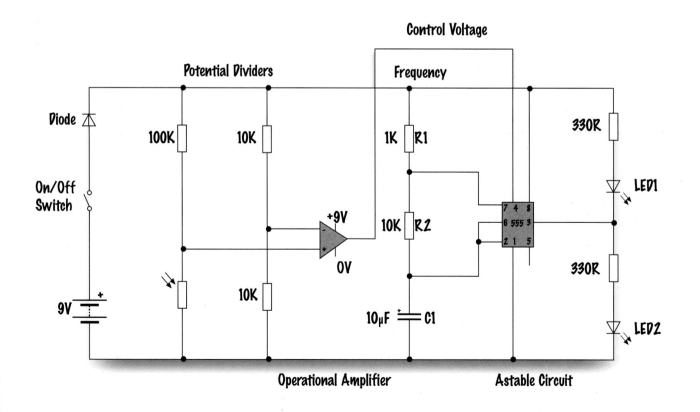

Logic Gates

LOGIC GATES are digital electronic devices which have several inputs and one output and are used to make decisions based on the condition of signals at the inputs. The name of each type of logic gate explains its function. The following are logic gates:

AND, OR, NOT, NAND, NOR, and **EXCLUSIVE OR**

Logic gates operate according to strict logical rules and their outputs only change when certain conditions are met at the inputs. The state of the output is controlled by the state of the inputs and the function or type of logic gate being used.

Logic gates are digital devices so their inputs and outputs will only ever be at LOGIC 1 (HIGH) or LOGIC 0 (LOW). The input signal to a logic gate has to be a digital signal. An analogue signal that is constantly changing by small amounts can confuse an electronic system that includes logic gates.

Analogue Signal

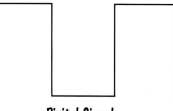

Digital Signal

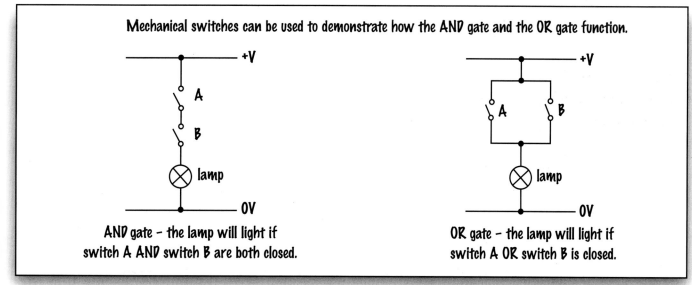

Mechanical switches can be used to demonstrate how the AND gate and the OR gate function.

AND gate – the lamp will light if switch A AND switch B are both closed.

OR gate – the lamp will light if switch A OR switch B is closed.

Logic gates can be made from discrete components but they are usually made as DIL ICs. They normally have a number of the same logic gates in the IC package. The gates operate separately but get their power from the same power supply to the IC.

Shown in the diagram is a 14 pin DIL package which contains four NAND gates.

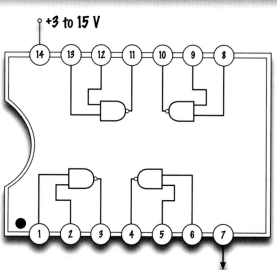

Symbols And Truth Tables

TRUTH TABLES list all the possible combinations of inputs and the resulting outputs. There are three basic logic gates: AND, OR and NOT. All other types of logic gates can be built from combinations of these basic gates.

The Two-Input AND Gate

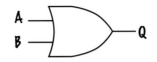

The output Q will be 1 when the inputs A and B are both 1.

A	B	Q
0	0	0
0	1	0
1	0	0
1	1	1

The Two-Input OR Gate

The output Q will be 1 when the inputs A or B are 1 or both inputs are 1.

A	B	Q
0	0	0
0	1	1
1	0	1
1	1	1

The NOT Gate

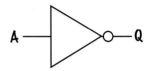

The NOT gate inverts (changes around) the signal. The output Q will be 1 when the input A is 0 and vice versa.

A	Q
0	1
1	0

The Two-Input NAND Gate

The truth table for a NAND gate is the opposite of the AND gate.

A	B	Q
0	0	1
0	1	1
1	0	1
1	1	0

A NAND gate can be built by connecting the output from an AND gate into the input of a NOT gate. A NAND gate means NOT AND.

A	B	Q1	Q2
0	0	0	1
0	1	0	1
1	0	0	1
1	1	1	0

The Two-Input NOR Gate

The truth table for a NOR gate is the opposite of the OR gate.

A	B	Q
0	0	1
0	1	0
1	0	0
1	1	0

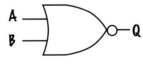

A NOR gate can be built by connecting the output from an OR gate into the input of a NOT gate. A NOR gate means NOT OR.

A	B	Q1	Q2
0	0	0	1
0	1	1	0
1	0	1	0
1	1	1	0

The Two-Input EXCLUSIVE OR Gate (XOR)

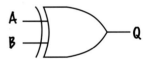

The EXCLUSIVE OR gate has been developed from the OR gate. It gives a high output if either of the inputs is high but a low output if both inputs are high or low. The EXCLUSIVE OR gate is a true OR function and was developed to remove the condition when both of its inputs were high and resulted in the OR gate functioning in a similar way to an AND gate. Compare the condition when A = 1 and B = 1 against the truth tables for the AND gate and the OR gate.

A	B	Q
0	0	0
0	1	1
1	0	1
1	1	0

Universal Building Block

The NAND logic gate is often referred to as the universal building block because every type of logic gate can be made by combining NAND gates. The advantage of using only NAND gates to construct logic circuits is that it reduces the number of different logic ICs in a circuit, resulting in a smaller PCB, reduced cost and less soldering and also removes the need to stock a wide range of logic ICs.

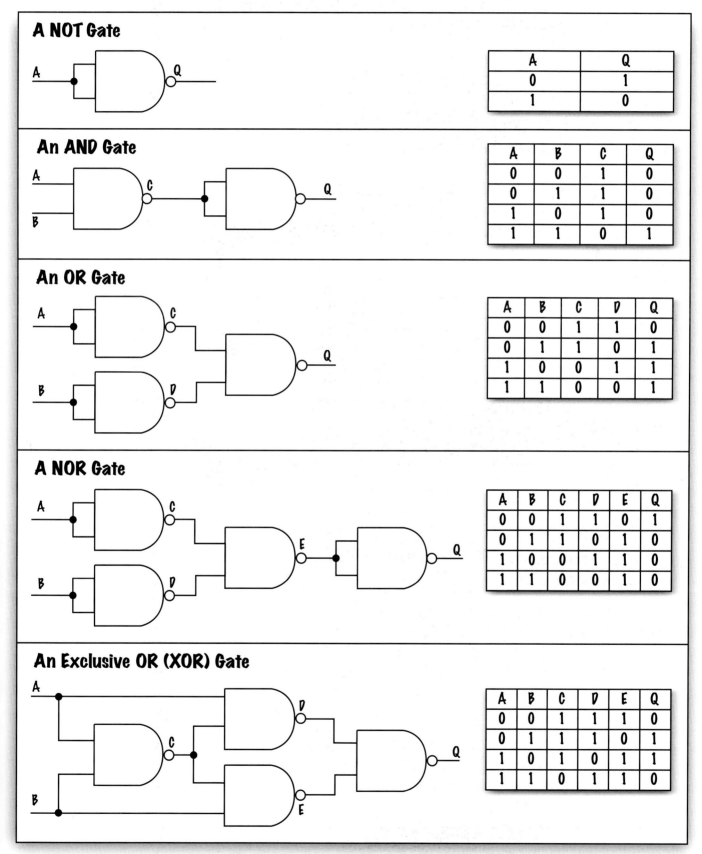

A NOT Gate

A	Q
0	1
1	0

An AND Gate

A	B	C	Q
0	0	1	0
0	1	1	0
1	0	1	0
1	1	0	1

An OR Gate

A	B	C	D	Q
0	0	1	1	0
0	1	1	0	1
1	0	0	1	1
1	1	0	0	1

A NOR Gate

A	B	C	D	E	Q
0	0	1	1	0	1
0	1	1	0	1	0
1	0	0	1	1	0
1	1	0	0	1	0

An Exclusive OR (XOR) Gate

A	B	C	D	E	Q
0	0	1	1	1	0
0	1	1	1	0	1
1	0	1	0	1	1
1	1	0	1	1	0

Astable Circuit Made From NAND Gates

Two NAND gates in combination with their inputs connected with a fixed resistor and a non-polarised capacitor makes an astable circuit with an equal mark-space ratio. The frequency of the astable can be altered by changing the fixed resistor to a variable resistor.

The value of C, the non-polarised capacitor, needs to be small (around 100nF) and the resistor therefore needs to have a high resistance value of around 1M5.

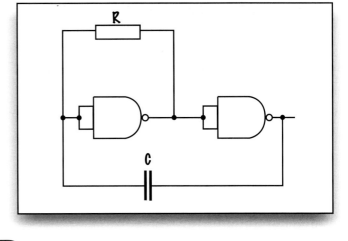

Time Delay Circuit Made From NAND Gates

A time delay can be made using two NAND gates in combination with their inputs connected. When the inputs to a NAND gate are connected in this way, it makes the NAND gate operate as a NOT gate, or inverter.

When the circuit is first connected to a power supply, the capacitor immediately starts to charge up through the resistor and the logic state on the input pins of gate A is 0. The logic 0 is inverted by gate A to logic 1 which is the input logic to gate B. Gate B inverts this logic 1 to logic 0.

When the voltage across the capacitor reaches a threshold level, the logic state on the input pins changes to logic 1. The logic 1 is inverted by gate A and the input on gate B becomes logic 0 which is then inverted again by gate B to logic 1.

The threshold level is the input voltage that is needed to change the output state of a logic gate. If a supply voltage of 5V is being used, then the threshold level is around 3.5V. With a 9V supply, the threshold is 8V.

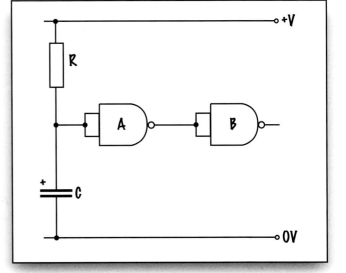

Logic Latch Made From NAND Gates

The diagram shows two NAND gates in combination with their inputs connected. Connecting the output of gate B to the input of gate A with a fixed resistor, R, makes a LOGIC LATCH. If the input to gate A is logic 1, output will be logic 0 which then becomes the input to gate B. The output to gate B would then be logic 1 which is returned back to the input of gate A by the feedback resistor, R, creating a latch. If the signal at gate A changes to logic 0, it will not break the latch due to the feedback resistor.

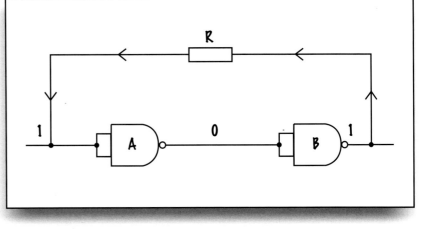

The CMOS 4017B decade counter is an extremely useful device which is easy to use and has many applications. The decade counter is available in a 16 pin DIL package and can operate between 3V and 15V. The 4017B consists of ten outputs which produce a sequential output. Only one output is high at any one time. If LEDs are connected to the output pins, they will each go high in their sequential order. The speed at which the LEDs come on and go off will depend on the speed of the pulse generator or clock which is connected to pin 14 of the decade counter. A very fast clock will make the LEDs appear as though they are all lit at the same time. If the ten LEDs are arranged sequentially in line, a rippling effect can be obtained as the LEDs go high then low.

For normal counting to take place, the clock enable (pin 13), the reset (pin 15) and the 'divide by 10' function (pin 12) should all be connected to 0 volts. Connecting one of the ten outputs directly to the reset (pin 15), causes the counter to reset back to the first output (pin 3). This is particularly useful when all ten outputs are not required, for example an electronic die circuit or a game which has to show lives lost. A push to make (PTM) switch can also be connected to pin 15 which provides a means of manually resetting the counter. The count can also be stopped by taking the clock enable (pin 13) high through a push to make (PTM) switch. Once the switch is released, the 4017B continues to count.

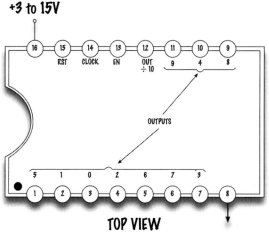

An Example Of A Decade Counter

The circuit diagram below is an example of a counting circuit using a 555 IC operating in the monostable mode set on a short time delay clocking into a 4017 IC decade counter. The circuit is being used as a steady hand game and after five lives have been lost, the thyristor latches and the buzzer sounds.

The monostable set on a short time delay is operating as a type of SCHMITT TRIGGER to eliminate switch bounce (see page 108). When the wand and track of the steady hand game touch, only one life can be lost approximately every two seconds. Whilst pin 3 of the monostable is high, the person playing the game is protected against switch bounce and can regain their composure. When the person has lost their fifth life, the 4017 decade counter sends a high signal to the gate of the thyristor which causes it to latch and the buzzer to sound. The reset switch is pressed to reset the decade counter and the reset switch across the thyristor is pressed to break the latch.

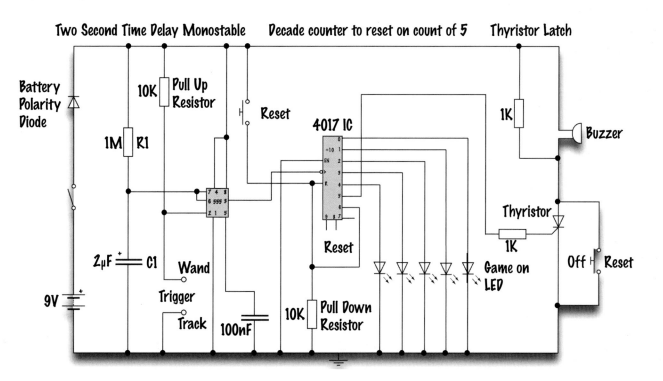

When mechanical switches are used in electronic circuits, it is sometimes necessary to overcome a problem known as SWITCH BOUNCE. Inside a mechanical switch there are small metal contacts which come together when the switch is closed to make a connection. When the switch is pressed and the contacts are nearly touching, there is the possibility of current jumping across the small gap and causing a rippling effect of on and off pulses. Unwanted pulses can also occur when the contacts come together and bounce back and forth rapidly when the switch is closed. In a counting circuit, switch bounce can cause a single count, made by a switch, to be registered as several counts.

There are a number of ways of eliminating switch bounce and one of the simplest ways is to use a **555 IC** monostable set on a very short time period.

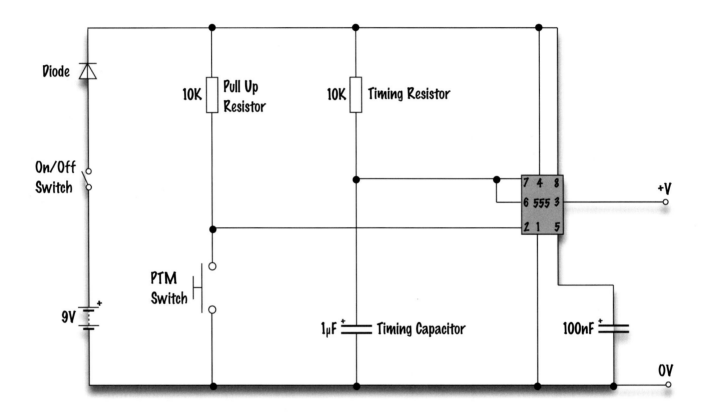

When the push to make (PTM) switch is pressed, pin 2 is taken to 0V and pin 3 goes high for a time period dependent upon the size of the timing resistor and the timing capacitor. This time period ($\approx C \times R$) will be greater than the total duration of the possible switch bounce.

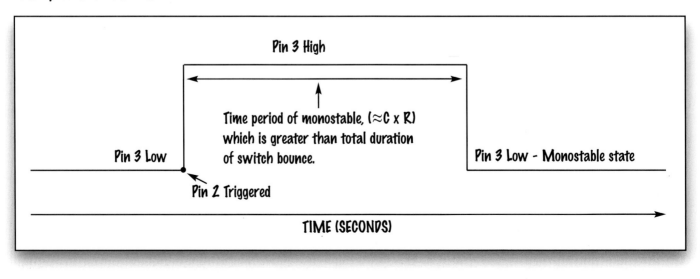

Schmitt Trigger

Another way of de-bouncing a switch is to use a special type of NAND gate called a SCHMITT TRIGGER. The device is available as a 14 pin DIL IC and contains four separate logic gates. The circuit symbol for a Schmitt Trigger is the same as the NAND gate symbol, with a hysteresis symbol (⎍) in the centre of the gate. A 4093 IC is a quad 2-input NAND Schmitt Trigger.

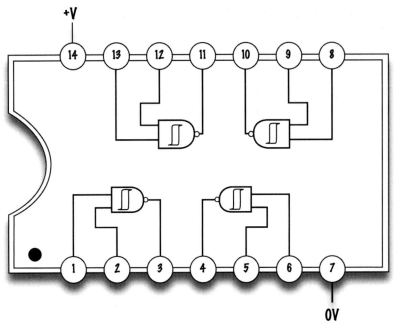

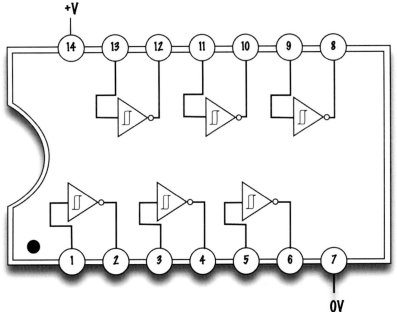

Also available is the 40106 IC which, again, is a Schmitt Trigger device and contains six separate Schmitt NOT gates. It is used in the same way as the 4093 IC.

Schmitt Trigger Switch Debouncing Circuit

When the switch is closed, switch bounce is prevented by the discharging action of the capacitor.

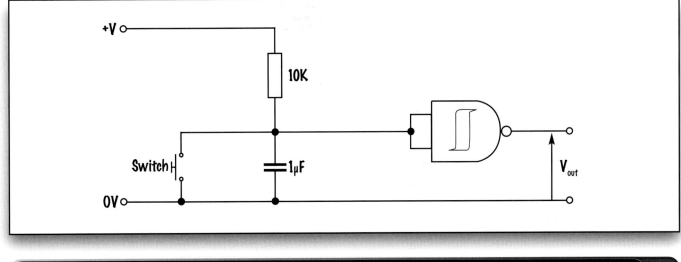

When the 555 IC was first introduced in 1972 it quickly became known as the timer in a chip due to the way it simplified the making of astable and monostable circuits. In a similar way, PICs are often referred to as the computer in a chip because they are essentially a computer in a special type of IC, which can be programmed to respond to input devices and control output devices. A PIC microcontroller includes a Central Processing Unit (CPU), Random Access Memory (RAM), Read Only Memory (ROM), a clock and input and output ports. A microcontroller therefore contains all of the units which are the basis of a microprocessor or computer. In a microprocessor system, each of these units will be made from one or more individual ICs, whereas the PIC microcontroller combines all of these units into a single IC.

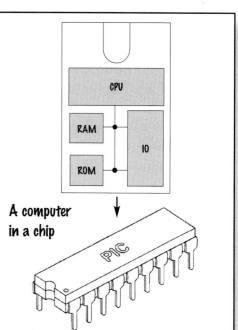

A computer in a chip

'PIC' identifies one product range belonging to Arizona Microchip Technology and stands for PERIPHERAL INTERFACE CONTROLLER. Many within the educational sector use the alternative names PROGRAMMABLE INTERFACE CONTROLLER or PROGRAMMABLE INTEGRATED CIRCUIT. Each year, millions of PIC microcontrollers are used in all types of consumer goods and industrial applications. PIC microcontrollers are widely used in daily life and can be found in stereo equipment, DVD players, mobile phones, toys, computer products and burglar alarms. A modern car can contain around 40 PICS which can be used for many purposes including controlling the management of the engine and controlling the temperature within the car for the passengers' comfort. A washing machine can have one or two PICs which control the whole washing cycle. Equally, a microwave oven can have a single PIC that processes information from the key pad and controls the various devices within the oven.

As a single PIC can replace a wide variety of traditional components such as transistors, logic circuits, timer circuits and counter circuits, manufacturers require smaller stock levels and the product assembly time can be reduced due to the smaller numbers of components. The final product will have fewer separate parts and is likely to be cheaper and more reliable. If the manufacturer wants to make changes to a product, all that is needed is to alter the programme without the need to re-design the PCB and change the components. By using PICs, manufacturers have greater flexibility – just by changing the programme and using a different case, a new product can be produced.

Types Of PICs

There are two main types of PIC microcontroller – FLASH devices and ONE-TIME PROGRAMMABLE (OTP) devices and they differ in the way they are programmed and erased.

Most PIC microcontrollers are FLASH reprogrammable which allows them to be erased electronically as many as 100,000 times. To change the programme (software), the PIC is placed in the programmer (hardware) and a new programme is downloaded to the PIC. Microcontrollers that can be reprogrammed have an F in their reference number, for example, PIC 16F627. All PICAXE microcontrollers are FLASH reprogrammable.

One-time programmable devices, as their name describes, can only be programmed once and if the programme is wrong, the PIC cannot be used again. Although there are versions of this type of PIC which have a small window that allows the programme to be erased by a special type of ultraviolet (UV) light source, there are serious health and safety considerations. The UV erasure units use a dangerous type of UV light compared to the type of UV light used in PCB exposure light boxes. OTP devices have a C in their reference number but are rarely used in education due to the dangers of the UV light source.

PIC Sizes

PIC microcontrollers are manufactured in a range of sizes including 8 pin, 18 pin, 28 pin and 40 pin. All are available in a dual in line. The larger PICs are more expensive but have a higher number of input and output pins. All sizes of PICs use the same BASIC language.

PICs can also vary in the amount of memory they have and this determines how big a programme can be downloaded into the chip. Some higher specification PICs have Analogue to Digital Conversion (ADC) built into them so that analogue sensors such as LDR and thermistors can be connected directly to the inputs.

THE MOST POPULAR PICAXE MICROCONTROLLERS USED IN SCHOOLS

PICAXE Range	IC Size	Memory (lines)	I/O Pins	Outputs	Inputs	ADC (L=low)	Data Memory	Polled Interrupt
PICAXE-08 12F629	8	40	5	1-4	1-4	1L	128 – prog	-
PICAXE-08M 12F683	8	80	5	1-4	1-4	3	256 - prog	Yes
PICAXE-18 16F627	18	40	13	8	5	3L	128 – prog	-
PICAXE-18A 16F619	18	80	13	8	5	3	256	Yes
PICAXE-18X 16F88	18	600	14	9	5	3	256 + 12c	Yes

Power Supply

PIC microcontrollers require a supply voltage of 3 to 5.5 DC which can be provided by AA alkaline cells of 1.5V.

4.5V can be provided by using 3 AA cells ... 1.5V x 3 = 4.5V.

If a diode is used in series with the AA cells, it will provide polarity protection for the PIC. As the diode has a 0.7 voltage drop across its leads, 4 AA cells can be used to give a voltage of 5.3V (4 x 1.5V - 0.7V = 5.3V) .

TIPS
Never use a 9V PP3 battery as this is well above the maximum voltage of 5.5V and will damage the PIC. Most AA battery holders use the same type of press-stud connector which fits the PP3 battery snap – be careful not to connect the PIC to a PP3 battery.

Resonators

Most modern PIC microcontrollers have an internal resonator which sets the speed at which the PIC microcontroller works (4MHz). Other types of PIC microcontrollers need to have an external 4MHz 3 pin ceramic resonator connected to the PIC microcontroller and the 0V power rail, for example, a 16F84 or 16F84A. The centre pin of the external resonator is connected to 0V and the two outer pins are connected to the two resonator pins. Resonators are not polar components and can be connected to the PIC microcontroller either way around.

8 Pin PIC Microcontrollers

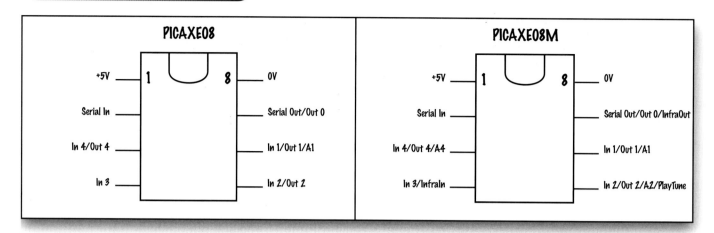

PICAXE08

+5V — 1	8 — 0V
Serial In	Serial Out/Out 0
In 4/Out 4	In 1/Out 1/A1
In 3	In 2/Out 2

PICAXE08M

+5V — 1	8 — 0V
Serial In	Serial Out/Out 0/InfraOut
In 4/Out 4/A4	In 1/Out 1/A1
In 3/InfraIn	In 2/Out 2/A2/PlayTune

18 Pin PIC Microcontrollers

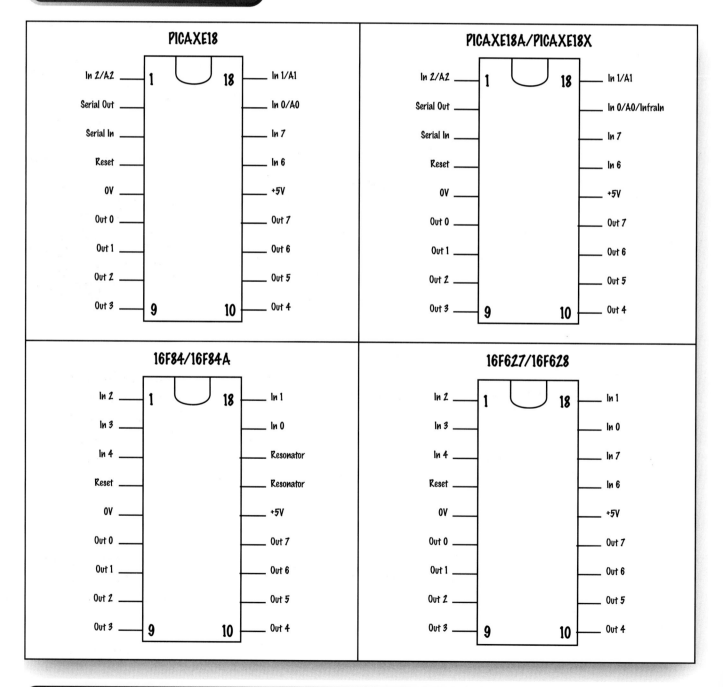

PICAXE18

In 2/A2 — 1	18 — In 1/A1
Serial Out	In 0/A0
Serial In	In 7
Reset	In 6
0V	+5V
Out 0	Out 7
Out 1	Out 6
Out 2	Out 5
Out 3 — 9	10 — Out 4

PICAXE18A/PICAXE18X

In 2/A2 — 1	18 — In 1/A1
Serial Out	In 0/A0/InfraIn
Serial In	In 7
Reset	In 6
0V	+5V
Out 0	Out 7
Out 1	Out 6
Out 2	Out 5
Out 3 — 9	10 — Out 4

16F84/16F84A

In 2 — 1	18 — In 1
In 3	In 0
In 4	Resonator
Reset	Resonator
0V	+5V
Out 0	Out 7
Out 1	Out 6
Out 2	Out 5
Out 3 — 9	10 — Out 4

16F627/16F628

In 2 — 1	18 — In 1
In 3	In 0
In 4	In 7
Reset	In 6
0V	+5V
Out 0	Out 7
Out 1	Out 6
Out 2	Out 5
Out 3 — 9	10 — Out 4

Machine Code

A PIC microcontroller is a programmable IC which is able to store sets of instructions in the form of a programme and carry out these instructions whenever the programme is run. The programmable code that a PIC microcontroller uses internally when carrying out the instructions in the programme is called MACHINE CODE and is very difficult to use and understand. Therefore, simpler programming languages are used to download instructions to the PIC. The internal machine code within the PIC is then generated automatically from the external programme.

Assembler Code

In industry, microcontrollers are programmed in a language called ASSEMBLER CODE which, like machine code, is also complicated and too advanced for most applications within the educational sector. Assembler code is an example of a low level programming language and requires a greater understanding of how PIC microprocessors work. The lower the level of programming language, the nearer it becomes to machine code and the harder it is to understand. The advantage of using a low-level programming language is that the finished programme is very concise, and runs faster and more efficiently.

BASIC And Flow Chart

High level programming languages, such as those used by PIC-Logicator and PICAXE, which use flow charts and BASIC (Beginners' All-purpose Symbolic Instruction Code) language, require very little knowledge of how PICs work and use commands which are easy to learn and understand. Many PIC programming systems support graphical programming where control systems are created as flow charts by dragging commands onto the screen and drawing routes between them. A number of these systems are able to convert flow charts automatically into a BASIC programme. The disadvantage of using high-level programming language is that it requires more of the PIC's memory space and runs slower.

Flow Chart Versus BASIC

Both ways of programming PIC microcontrollers use the same BASIC language commands. BASIC is a text-based language that is used throughout the world to programme everything from PICs to personal computers. The flow chart method provides a user-friendly graphical way of joining the BASIC language commands together and greatly reduces the need for keyboard skills.

Flow chart programming uses a smaller number of BASIC commands and is favoured by the educational sector. Complicated and large programmes are best written in BASIC which has a greater number of commands and is a more powerful way of programming PIC microcontrollers.

Flow Chart Symbols

A flow chart shows the order in which a series of commands are carried out, in other words, the sequence of events in which something is controlled. There are different specific symbols for each command and they are linked together by arrows to show the correct sequence of events. Some symbols are shown below.

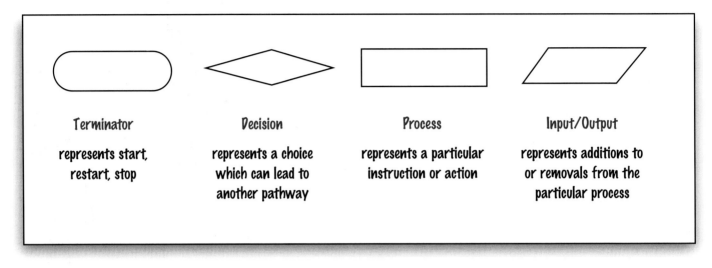

Terminator	Decision	Process	Input/Output
represents start, restart, stop	represents a choice which can lead to another pathway	represents a particular instruction or action	represents additions to or removals from the particular process

Flow Chart And BASIC

The two programmes shown below will make output 2 of a PIC microcontroller go high for one second and then low for one second and then repeat the process until the power is disconnected from the PIC.

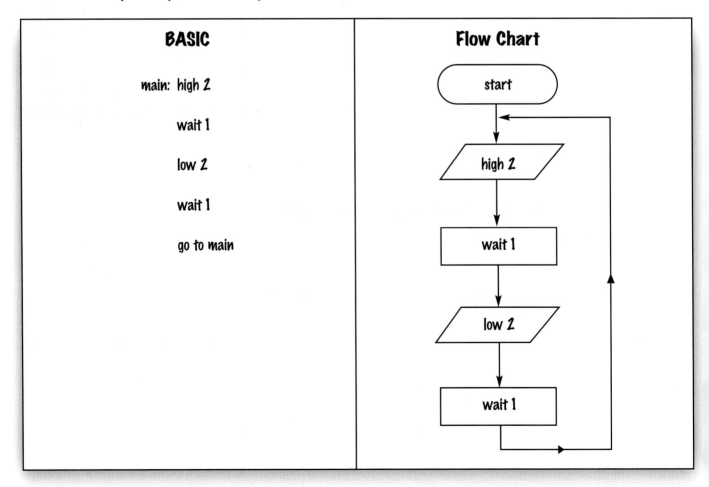

BASIC

main: high 2

wait 1

low 2

wait 1

go to main

Flow Chart

start → high 2 → wait 1 → low 2 → wait 1

The Decimal System

The everyday decimal system of counting uses ten digits, 0 to 9. When the count exceeds 9, a 1 is placed in a second column to the left of the units column to represent 10s. A third column to the left of the 10s column gives 100s and then 1000s and so on. The values of the columns starting from the right are: 1, 10, 100, 1000, or in powers of 10: 10^0, 10^1, 10^2, 10^3 etc.

The Binary System

Digital electronics process digital signals which only have two states, HIGH which equals 1, and LOW which equals 0, and therefore cannot use the decimal system of counting which uses ten digits. Counting in digital circuits uses a counting system called BINARY which only has two digits, 0 and 1, and counts in powers of 2. The binary digits 0 and 1 are called BITS (derived from 'binary digits'). Eight BITS make one BYTE. When counting in binary, many more columns are needed in comparison to counting in decimal. For example, 11111111 in binary equals 255.

Successive columns from the right represent the binary numbers in powers of 2, i.e. 2^0, 2^1, 2^2, and 2^3 which in decimal would be 1, 2, 4 and 8. The table alongside shows how the decimal numbers 0 to 15 are coded in binary and require four bits to give 1111 which equals 15 decimal. The column on the extreme right is called the LEAST SIGNIFICANT BIT (LSB) and the column on the extreme left is called the MOST SIGNIFICANT BIT (MSB).

THE BINARY SYSTEM OF COUNTING				
MSB			LSB	
2^3 (8)	2^2 (4)	2^1 (2)	2^0 (1)	Decimal
0	0	0	0	0
0	0	0	1	1
0	0	1	0	2
0	0	1	1	3
0	1	0	0	4
0	1	0	1	5
0	1	1	0	6
0	1	1	1	7
1	0	0	0	8
1	0	0	1	9
1	0	1	0	10
1	0	1	1	11
1	1	0	0	12
1	1	0	1	13
1	1	1	0	14
1	1	1	1	15

Converting Binary Numbers To Decimal Numbers

Let the binary number be 1011

$1011 = (1 \times 2^3) + (0 \times 2^2) + (1 \times 2^1) + (1 \times 2^0)$

$1011 = 8 + 0 + 2 + 1$

$1011 = 11$ decimal

Converting Decimal Numbers To Binary Numbers

Continuously divide the decimal number by 2 and record the remainder after each division. The remainder will be either 0 or 1 and this forms the binary number.

Let the decimal number be 11

$11 \div 2 = 5$ remainder 1

$5 \div 2 = 2$ remainder 1

$2 \div 2 = 1$ remainder 0

$1 \div 2 = 0$ remainder 1

decimal 11 =   (MSB) 1   0   1   1 (LSB) binary

Using Binary Numbers

When working with PIC microcontrollers, it is sometimes easier to work in the binary system of counting, especially when trying to control many outputs at the same time.

The following PICAXE programme demonstrates how to make a 7-segment display count from 0 to 9. The % sign tells the PIC microcontroller that binary is being used instead of decimal. The PIC output pins are connected to the segments of the display as shown below. This means that all 8 outputs can be controlled at the same time.

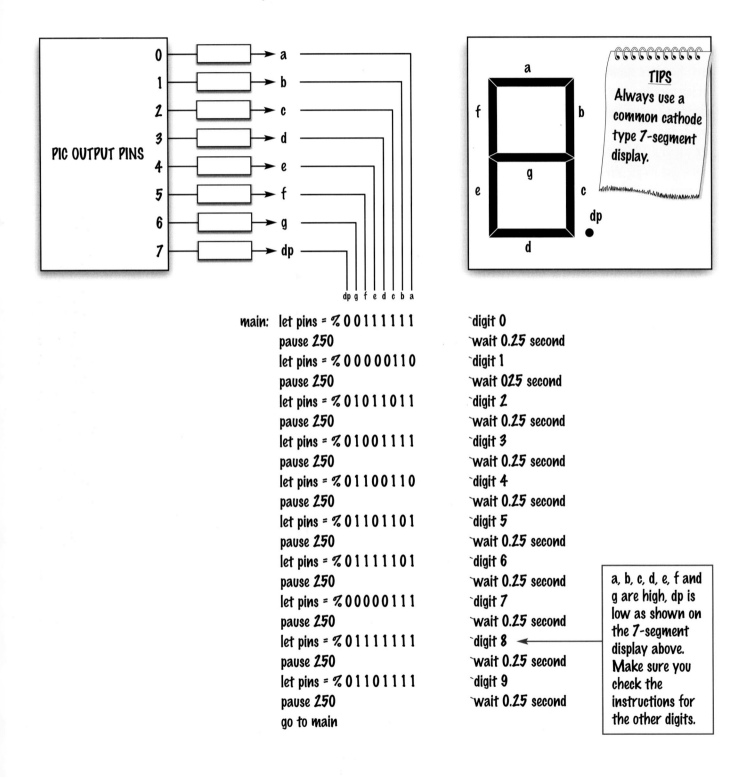

TIPS
Always use a common cathode type 7-segment display.

```
main:   let pins = %00111111    `digit 0
        pause 250               `wait 0.25 second
        let pins = %00000110    `digit 1
        pause 250               `wait 025 second
        let pins = %01011011    `digit 2
        pause 250               `wait 0.25 second
        let pins = %01001111    `digit 3
        pause 250               `wait 0.25 second
        let pins = %01100110    `digit 4
        pause 250               `wait 0.25 second
        let pins = %01101101    `digit 5
        pause 250               `wait 0.25 second
        let pins = %01111101    `digit 6
        pause 250               `wait 0.25 second
        let pins = %00000111    `digit 7
        pause 250               `wait 0.25 second
        let pins = %01111111    `digit 8
        pause 250               `wait 0.25 second
        let pins = %01101111    `digit 9
        pause 250               `wait 0.25 second
        go to main
```

a, b, c, d, e, f and g are high, dp is low as shown on the 7-segment display above. Make sure you check the instructions for the other digits.

Below is shown a PIC-Logicator flow chart version of the programme to make a 7-segment display count from 0 to 9. As the flow chart runs, the digital panel shows the changing state of outputs and inputs as they would be if the flow chart had been downloaded to a PIC microcontroller.

The memory bar in the bottom right-hand corner of the flow chart shows the amount of memory available in the PIC.

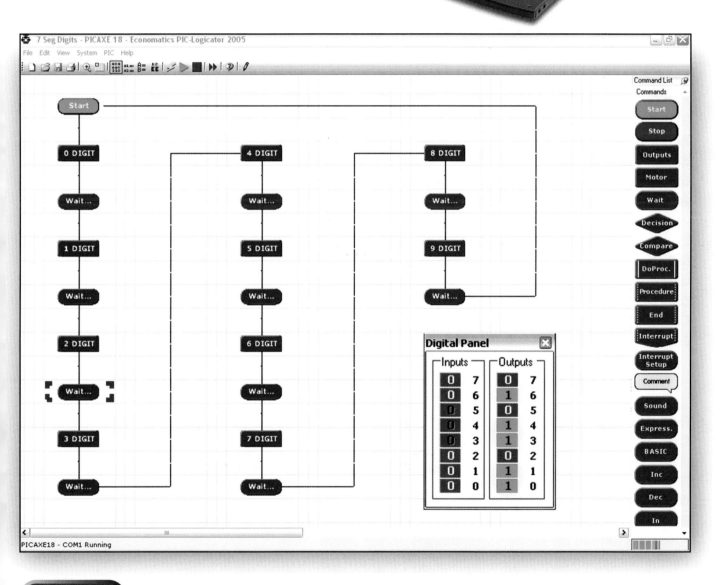

Summary

- PICs are programmable devices.
- PICs are purchased BLANK and then programmed with a specific control programme.
- Most PICs are FLASH reprogrammable which allows them to be erased.
- PICs require a voltage supply of 3 to 5.5 DC.
- PICs are the brain of an electronic system and can bring greater intelligence to the process section.
- Complicated logic circuits are made simpler by using a PIC.

INDEX

INDEX

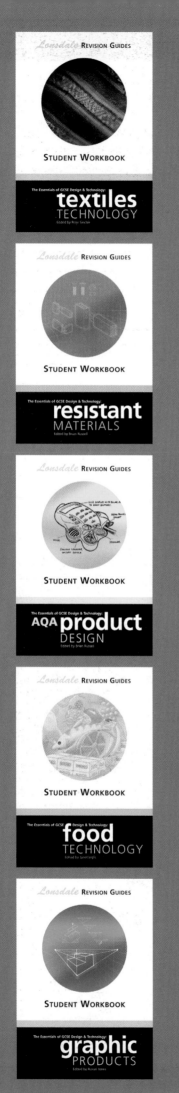

The Essentials of
Design and Technology

Designed to cover the core features of the relevant specifications, these guides present the subject matter in a visually attractive, unintimidating way, taking account of different learning styles. They are perfect for use throughout the course or as an exam revision aid in the final stages of preparation for the GCSE.

A valuable aid for both teachers and pupils.

now supported by value-for-money Workbooks.

A fantastic resource for both teachers and pupils. Use them as ...

- Classwork sheets
- to be used with or without the guides.
- Easy-to-mark homework sheets
- useful for learning or testing understanding.
- Test material
- concentrates on particular topics.
- Structured revision
- tests knowledge prior to the Examination.